397

C198   Earl Swartzentruber   10—
                                PH

Jenny Lind's America

§§   Other Books by Frances Cavanah

Abe Lincoln Gets His Chance
*Adventure in Courage: The Story of
    Theodore Roosevelt*
Holiday Roundup
Jenny Lind and Her Listening Cat
Our Country's Freedom
Our Country's Story
*The Secret of Madame Doll: A Story of the
    American Revolution*
*Triumphant Adventure: The Story of
    Franklin Delano Roosevelt*
We Came to America

§§   In collaboration with Elizabeth L. Crandal

*Freedom Encyclopedia: American Liberties in
    the Making*
Meet the Presidents

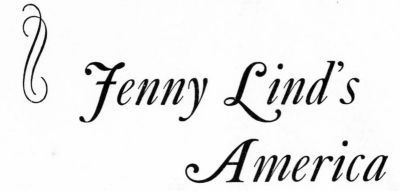

Jenny Lind's America

Frances Cavanah

Chilton Book Company
Philadelphia · New York · London

Portions of this book appeared in another form
under the title Two Loves for Jenny Lind.
New material based on new research has been added,
especially concerning the latter part of
Jenny Lind's American tour.

§ *To Muriel Fuller, Friend and Critic,*
For whose wise counsel
I am deeply grateful

Contents

three § *Two Loves for a Nightingale*

The Memory Lingers On

After the final encore at a Jenny Lind concert in Washington, one woman in the audience turned to another.

"I feel as though I have parted from a dear friend," she said.

This was not an unusual reaction, for the Swedish Nightingale had a remarkable ability for establishing rapport with her listeners. It was not only her superb voice, but also her personality that helped to hold her listeners spellbound. She did this without the aid of physical beauty, but there is abundant testimony that she gave the illusion of beauty when she sang.

What happened to the thousands who attended her concerts can also happen to an author. One finds it hard to say good-by to Jenny Lind. I have written about her before, in magazines and books, and the subject still enthralls me.

In the present volume I have concentrated on her American tour and the events that led up to it. The twenty-one months she spent in the United States were important for both the prima donna and the exuberant young country that first welcomed her in September, 1850. They were important for Jenny Lind, because it was here that her two loves, her love of music and her love for the man she married, were blended in a rich fulfillment. They were important for the American nation, since she was the first great musician to visit our shores at the height of her powers. Probably more than any one person she helped to awaken the American people to an appreciation of good music.

It must have been an interesting experience for a foreigner to visit the United States in the middle of the last century. The population had reached what then seemed the astonishing number of twenty-three million people, and thousands of immigrants were arriving every year. With the recent acquisition of California, the nation extended across the continent from the Atlantic to the Pacific, and California was admitted as the thirty-first state in the Union shortly after Jenny Lind's arrival.

A great age of invention had begun. The "magnetic telegraph" had been in operation only a few years. Miss Lind had crossed the Atlantic "on wings of steam," in the florid words of one newspaper, but steamships were still something of a novelty. The introduction of the steam railroad made possible her extensive concert tour under the management of Phineas T. Barnum, though between a few of the towns on her itinerary it was necessary to travel by stage-coach.

Yes, there was progress in the United States and also a great deal of social ferment. A few "radical" women were actually demanding the right to vote—a shocking idea to most of their male contemporaries. Slavery was the question uppermost in nearly everyone's mind, and after reading the anti-slavery novel by Harriet Beecher Stowe, Jenny wrote the author a "fan" letter.

I have a feeling about Uncle Tom's Cabin—she said—*that great changes will take place by and by.*

Jenny Lind contributed to an anti-slavery fund being raised by Mrs. Stowe. It was one of many causes to which the famous visitor made generous donations. Sincerely religious, she felt that her voice was a gift from God and that it was both a duty and a privilege to give a large proportion of her earnings to worthy causes. That canny showman, P.T. Barnum, took this into account when he decided to risk his entire fortune to bring her to the United States. He sensed that what he called "this peculiarity in her character" would appeal to the American church-going public. In his publicity campaign, the first of its kind in America, Jenny's reputation as a lady bountiful was given equal emphasis with the bell-like tones of her voice.

Fortunately for P.T. Barnum's bank account, Jenny lived up to her publicity, and sometimes the enthusiasm of an audience verged on hysteria. *Should we attempt to express all we felt, our readers would suspect us of having lost our wits,* stated one Washington newspaper. Some reporters were less restrained and their extravagant phrases would sound laughable today. In viewing Jenny Lind, it must be against the sentimental background of her own times. Yet sentimentality can assume different guises. The incident where Jenny dropped her shawl, only to have a crowd pounce on it and tear it into tiny pieces as souvenirs, is no more farfetched than some of the antics of admirers of popular singers of our own time.

As could be expected, there were some dissenting opinions. A few people, very few, indeed, were unmoved by her voice. Toward the end of her stay, after she left the Barnum management, she sometimes had an unfriendly press. She was said to be stubborn and unpredictable, and fortunately she had enough human frailties to be interesting. Otherwise, she would have been too good to be true.

The fact remains that she was probably more deeply loved than any of the bright stars of stage and concert platform, and more recently of movies and television, who have succeeded her. As always in such cases, her appeal lay in intangibles. Her voice was only one facet of a luminous personality.

Since there are no recordings of her voice, that then must be the explanation of her continuing appeal. The year of her sesquicentennial, 1970, finds her still remembered and admired, and not many one hundred and fifty-year-old ladies have kept such a firm hold on the public. The young nation she visited is not so young now, and it is more sophisticated. Many ideas about music have changed and will continue to change, but pendulums have a way of swinging back and forth. Taste comes full circle, and the old and tried becomes popular again.

After a century and a half Jenny Lind stands alone. Even her name is like a song, and to paraphrase Irving Berlin, the memory lingers on.

Frances Cavanah
Washington, D. C.
April 30, 1969

Author's Note

In this book, which takes the form of a biographical novel, the facts are substantially as presented. Minor liberties were taken necessarily with chronology, inasmuch as the exact sequence of events was not always known. Also, in actual life, Jenny Lind encountered similar experiences at different times and in many different places; certain incidents were described at that point in the story where they seemed to fit most naturally.

The Lind letters were carefully studied to gain an insight into her thinking and to learn certain turns of phrase which she might have used in conversation. In recording some of the dialogue of a personal nature, it was necessary to draw on the imagination, but such conversations might logically have taken place in the light of known circumstances. Letters and also contemporary accounts furnished important clues.

Research included not only standard biographies but books of reminiscences and magazine articles by persons who had had contact with the Swedish Nightingale. Original sources, which made available unpublished letters and a wealth of newspaper clippings, furnished fresh and interesting information. Jenny's American tour was followed through newspaper files and local histories of the cities that she visited. These histories and newspapers were especially rewarding—and sometimes the only source of information —on concerts she gave in Toronto and New York State after she left the management of P. T. Barnum.

For aid in research I am much indebted to the librarians at the Library of Congress in Washington, D.C., the Lincoln Center Branch of The New York Public Library, and the librarians and curators of a number of museums who responded generously to my request for information. I am deeply grateful to Dr. Zonia Wallen Lawrence for her translations from the Swedish of several letters not available in English.

Of further help in visualizing the Swedish Nightingale were visits to some of the places that had special meaning to her. An interesting morning was spent with Mrs. E. Sohier Welch, the present owner of the charming old house in Boston's Louisburg Square where Jenny Lind was married. Mrs. Margaret Grierson, former curator of the Sophia Smith Collection of the Smith College Library, was my guide in Northampton. It was in this town in the Berkshires, dubbed by Jenny "the paradise of America," that she and her husband spent their honeymoon.

I have enjoyed reading and writing about Jenny Lind. Another pleasure was seeing the exquisite doll replicas of the real-life heroine of this book. These dolls by the well known doll designer, Madame B. Alexander, were created as a special sesquicentennial tribute to the memory of the Swedish Nightingale.

Portrait of Jenny Lind from life. Owned in 1935 by Edward Bryant of London.

one
Prelude to America

I $§§$

The Real Jenny Lind

Jenny glanced down at the sleeping infant in her arms.

"Ah, your mother has something to live for," she said.

She kissed the baby's heel. She planted another kiss on the back of his neck, a gesture that in her native Sweden symbolized a blessing for a child. For a few minutes in this quiet English garden she could feel, or pretend to feel, that the child was really hers. But a jarring bit of doggerel kept running through her mind:

> *Jenny Lind O! Jenny Lind O!*
> *Come to the window.*

She had heard it often enough on her recent tour through England. At her hotel, in nearly every town, a crowd had gathered below her balcony to chant the words again and again. It was really intended for quite another Jenny Lind, she reflected. That other Jenny, queen of song and known as "the Swedish Nightingale," was a famous opera star and actress, the friend of kings and queens. In whatever city she sang there was a rush to buy tickets. In London the crowds had been so great that the phrase, "a Jenny Lind crush," had become a byword. She was admired as much by the humble as by the great; and her picture hung on a wall in many a remote cottage whose occupants had never heard her sing a single golden note.

The pictures showed a young woman with strong, irregular features, who for some indefinable reason created an illusion of beauty. Jenny considered herself plain and was frankly puzzled by the extravagant admiration of the public. The real Jenny Lind, she was convinced, was not the exhausted opera star who curtsied before a wildly cheering audience at the end of a performance. The self she most desired to be sat in the garden of Clairville Cottage, the little white house she had rented in a quiet section of the city. She might be the star of the London Opera, but the real Jenny cuddled another woman's baby in her arms. The queen of song, the toast of Europe, lavished her affection on the coachman's family.

But not for long, she thought. By this time next year or the year after—

There was a sudden chill in the April air. Jenny took off her shawl and wrapped it around the baby. Why should there be this nagging doubt in the back of her mind, when she was to have what she had long yearned for? After a series of farewell performances for Mr. Lumley, her English manager, she was leaving the stage. She would continue to sing in concerts for she still needed money. Not for herself but for the scholarships she planned to endow in Stockholm —scholarships to help poor but worthy students such as she had once been.

In another month she was to be married. Then she would be free of the almost unbearable fatigue which life in the theater, despite all the glitter of her success, had imposed on her since she was a child. She had planned to retire before this but had yielded to the pleas of Mr. Lumley to extend her engagement. His fortunes were at low ebb. If she would consent to appear only six more times in his theater, he had assured her, she could save him from financial ruin.

That she should want to retire at all was hard for her admirers to understand. At twenty-eight she was at the height of her success. Only a few close friends knew how intensely she lived every role, how much her performances took out of her. Nor did many people know the other reason for her decision. What Jenny wanted most in the world, she had once written a friend, was to find "a being to love," to whom she could "entirely and utterly" surrender herelf.

Now at last she had found him. She was betrothed to Captain Claudius Harris who lived in the famous old English town of Bath. He was a relative of her friend, Mrs. Grote.

"What a dull young man!" That had been Jenny's reaction at their first meeting. Now that they knew each other better she wondered how she could have been so wrong. Though Claudius was only twenty-three, five years younger than Jenny, they had so much in common. They shared an interest in religion, and Claudius was so good, so handsome. Later that afternoon he was calling to discuss their marriage settlement.

The wedding was to be in May, here in the garden. The trees would be in full leaf by then, and perhaps the rose vine over the trellis would be in bloom.

Not that Captain Harris was the first to love Jenny Lind. Among others, there had been Hans Christian Andersen, who had treated her like one of the princesses in his fairy tales. Poor Brother Hans! She was afraid she had hurt him cruelly. She was very fond of him, but that was all.

And before that? Jenny flushed even now at the memory of Adolf Lindblad, the well-known Swedish composer. Her own home, with a sharp-tongued mother and a charming but indolent and alcoholic father, was marred by bickering. In such an atmosphere she knew that her career was threatened and the Lindblads had suggested that she live with them. Here Jenny's need for affection had been her undoing. She was nineteen, Adolf thirty-eight, when they fell in love. Sophie Lindblad, who adored her husband, would have consented to a divorce if it would make him happy. But Jenny was shocked at the thought of breaking up the marriage of two beloved friends. Sophie had been like a mother to her, and the temperamental Adolf, whatever his feelings might be at the moment, needed the calm, reassuring presence of his wife.

It was Jenny Lind's first experience with love—and a heartbreaking one. Her abrupt departure to give concerts in Finland was her way of handling a situation that threatened to get out of control.

Later, she had become engaged to Julius Gunther, a fellow artist in the Swedish Opera. The theater was his life. To him it was absurd, it was incomprehensible, that she should ever want to leave it. Finally, they had been forced to admit that they could not hope to find happiness together.

A short time before a talented German student, Otto Goldschmidt, had come on from Germany to play her accompaniments in some benefit concerts. There was something very appealing about the tall, dark young man with the gentle manners and Jenny suspected that he was a little in love with her, too. But he was only a boy, not quite twenty. She had wanted to help him, because he had been a friend of Felix Mendelssohn.

At the thought of Herr Mendelssohn, Jenny's eyes misted. Although this gifted musician had been dead for nearly a year and a half, she still could not think of him without tears. Never had she known such happiness, such a lifting of the spirit, as in his company.

Jenny was still grieving over the loss of Mendelssohn's wise counsel and her broken engagement to Julius Gunther when she met Captain Harris. He was not a musician, and for that very reason she had turned to him more readily. Perhaps there would be fewer problems with one who had never entered the exacting world of music.

"Captain Harris is here."

Jenny had been too absorbed in her memories to notice the approach of her friend and traveling companion, Josephine Ahmansson. Josephine's broad, solemn face broke into a smile as she held out her arms.

"Shall I take the little one back to the coachman's cottage?"

Jenny held the baby closer for an instant before she surrendered him.

"Please give his mother my thanks for allowing me to borrow him for a while. But isn't Claudius early?"

"He said to beg your pardon," Josephine replied, "but he couldn't wait."

Dear Claudius, thought Jenny, as she ran lightly across the lawn. He was always so impatient. She knew why he was early; the last time he was here they had quarreled. It was nothing serious, but his prejudice against the theater always distressed Jenny. In the entryway she paused before a mirror to fix her hair, which had become slightly disheveled in the garden. Then, unable to restrain her own impatience, she threw open the door of the drawing room. For a moment she let her eyes rest on the tall, blond figure. Each time she was away from Captain Harris, she wondered if perhaps love had colored her remembrance. Each time she saw him, he appeared even more handsome than she had thought.

"Claudius!" she went toward him, her hands outstretched.

"Jenny! Darling!" He had barely kissed her when he started to apologize. "I hope you won't think it improper—

my coming early. I arrived in London sooner than I had expected. Rather than waste an hour when we had so much to discuss—"

"I am glad you came. To be sure," she said demurely, "I had planned a more impressive entrance."

An unruly strand of hair, yellow as honey, had come loose again. Captain Harris pushed it back from her forehead.

"Yes, and to have my hair combed," she laughed. "Oh, Claudius—"

She was in his arms. It was the moment for which both had been waiting, and the problems which had been troubling them seemed suddenly very trivial.

"Please! *Please!*" Jenny drew away from him. "You must give me a chance to look at you."

Claudius came out of his daze, every inch the proper army officer again.

"As I said"—he cleared his throat self-consciously—"we have much to decide. The terms of the marriage settlement —the location of our future home—"

"Yes, I have just written Judge Munthe, my guardian—"

"Why must you have a guardian?" Claudius cut in sharply. "Your parents are both living."

Some of the joy had gone out of Jenny's face. Somewhat haltingly she explained that her father, Jonas Lind, and her mother, Anne-Marie, now lived in the country, too far from Stockholm to assume any responsibility for their daughter. According to Swedish law, every unmarried woman, no matter what her age, must have a legal guardian, and she had chosen Henric Munthe, a highly respected judge.

"He has been like a father to me ever since," she said. "I have just written him, asking that he inquire about some suitable place in the country where we might like to live after our marriage."

"Impossible!" said Claudius. "We must make our home in England."

"Very well. I want you to see my own dear Sweden, but I love England, too. In fact—" she smiled as she slipped her hand into his and led him to the windowseat—"I think it is very nice of you to be an Englishman."

Claudius, pleased by her easy surrender, touched his lips to her hair. "There is a convenient cottage near my mother's home in Bath that I can buy."

This time Jenny was a little slower to agree.

"I suppose it doesn't matter, so long as we can live quietly. I would like to be near water and woods and a cathedral. Oh, *Älskade* (beloved) Claudius, I doubt if you can understand how much it will mean to me to have a real home. I never did, you know, even as a child."

"But, why, Jenny? Even when you were attending the Theatre School in Stockholm, you lived at home most of the time."

"Yes, but a home must have love in it, or it is no home at all."

She wanted to go on, to share with him her bitter secret. In all honesty she supposed she should confide in her future husband, but something held her back. Perhaps it was a grudging admiration for her mother. Or it may have been the memory, despite her later disillusionment, of the way she had adored her father as a child.

"You have told me very little about your parents," Captain Harris persisted.

At the note of suspicion in his voice Jenny stiffened and drew away from him.

"My father was a very sweet person and a good musician. I think he may have wanted to earn a living for us, but—"

She paused, then forced herself to go on.

"My—my mother had to work very hard, harder than she should. For a while she kept a school for girls. Sometimes she went out as a governess. She had many trials which I did not always understand while I was growing up. I thought her very harsh."

"Why, Jenny!" the Captain was shocked. "That attitude is most unscriptural. Does not the Fifth Commandment say —"

"I know what the Fifth Commandment says," she replied sharply, then added in a softer voice, "I do honor my parents, Claudius. I spent almost my first earnings to buy them a home."

"That was—er—noble of you."

"Not at all. Now that my mother is not worried about money, she is happier than I ever thought she could be."

"Forgive me, darling," said Claudius. "I should know that everyone is not blessed with a mother like mine. I have assured her that you are the purest soul who ever lived, even if you are an actress."

He was so deeply stirred by his own apology that Jenny's reaction to it came as a shock. She jumped up and stood glaring down at him.

"Do I have to say it again?" she demanded. "I am giving up the stage. I *want* to give it up, but I must make one thing clear to you. I am leaving the theater, but I will never be ashamed of it."

"Not ashamed?" At this show of defiance, Claudius felt his own anger rise. As Jenny's future husband, he must begin to assert himself. "Not ashamed that your picture is stuck in every workman's window, that your name is on every Cockney's tongue? How do you think it makes me feel—me a respected army officer who serves his queen—"

He paused, confused. Queen Victoria was one of Jenny's most admiring friends.

"Of course"—he squirmed under Jenny's steadfast gaze —"I realize that all this vulgar excitement is distasteful to you, too, and I do not reproach you about the past. I have faith that you resisted the temptations of the theater—"

"I have not resisted them." Jenny bridled. "I have simply not been tempted, and I do not intend to spend the rest of my life repenting sins I have never committed. For you to imply that an opera singer is necessarily a handmaiden of the devil is to cast a slur on the gift that God gave me—"

"That God gave you?" To Claudius, Jenny's assumption that her talent was a divine gift, to be used for the good of her fellowmen, was close to blasphemy.

"Yes," said Jenny firmly. "I have tried to do good with my voice. I shall go on doing good with it."

"I thought you were leaving the stage," Captain Harris reminded her.

"You know I plan to sing in concerts. You know how close my charities are to my heart. They are my way of giving thanks for the gift that I have been blessed with. If we do not agree about this, it will be better that we say goodby."

Claudius jumped up and stood towering over her. Jenny saw her own misery reflected in his eyes.

"Don't say it," he begged. "Don't ever say that you won't marry me. I couldn't bear it."

"Nor I," she replied simply.

Again she was in his arms, her words muffled against his shoulder.

"Can't you see, Claudius, that I need love—much love? I shall ask for nothing else in the world, except you, once I am free."

"You are free now," he insisted. "You need never enter that temple of Satan again."

"*Mon Dieu!*" The reconciliation was shortlived. Jenny flung herself away from him, eyes blazing. "I shall be obliged to enter that temple of Sata*n*"—she bore down on the words, unconsciously mimicking the captain's righteous tone—"quite a few more times. Have you forgotten my six farewell appearances for Mr. Lumley? That was our understanding. Remember?"

"Well, yes," Claudius admitted. "But you knew I disapproved. After talking it over with my mother—"

"Your mother has nothing to do with this. It is my duty to keep my promise to my manager."

"And what of the duty of a wife to obey her husband?" he demanded hotly.

"I am not your wife yet. Claudius, be reasonable. I have signed a contract with Mr. Lumley. What does it matter if I must make one final personal sacrifice?"

"Even the sacrifice of our marriage?"

Jenny paused. A long pause. "Even that, if you force me to a decision."

It was not the answer Captain Harris had expected. "Don't"—his voice broke—"don't say it again."

"What else can I say? We have quarreled *again*, this time beyond all help."

"Not beyond help," Captain Harris protested. "Perhaps Mr. Nassau Senior can help us."

This elderly solicitor, a friend of Mrs. Grote's, was the lawyer who had agreed to draw up the couple's marriage settlement, and, since there was not time to write Judge Munthe, she knew she could depend on Mr. Senior for advice. He was both wise and kind. Claudius thought he saw a flicker of hope in Jenny's face. He was quick to follow up this advantage.

"Yes," he went on more confidently, "Mr. Senior may be able to get you out of your contract with this Lumley." Then, desperately, when Jenny did not answer, "At least, say that you will talk to him."

"All right, Claudius."

"But the marriage settlement." He fumbled in his waistcoat pocket and brought out a folded paper. "I feel strongly, and my mother agrees with me, that it would be unscriptural—"

"What have I done now that is unscriptural?" Jenny tried, not very successfully, to control the fury in her voice.

"Nothing," he said hastily, "I am only trying to safeguard your future. I have jotted down a few of my re—my suggestions—"

"Give me the paper, please." Jenny held out her hand for it. Then abruptly, "Goodby, Claudius."

"Goodby?" he stammered. "When do I see you again?"

"After I have made my decision about Mr. Lumley."

"Have you nothing more to say?"

"Can you not see how I am torn to pieces by these quarrels?" She turned her face away and looked out into the garden. "And now—please go!"

2 §§

Outraged Prima Donna

Jenny heard the reluctant footsteps across the carpeted floor, then a click as Captain Harris closed the door behind him. Finally she turned, her eyes taking in every detail of the little drawing room: the gay chintz curtains, the vases overflowing with flowers, the fire crackling on the hearth. How often she had liked to imagine that Clairville Cottage was really her own; that when she heard the wheels of a carriage on the cobbled street, it would be her husband— tall, handsome Captain Harris—coming home for tea.

With a feeling almost of foreboding, Jenny opened the folded paper in her hand and forced herself to read it. She rose and, with an angry swish of skirts, walked across the room to her writing desk. She drew a piece of notepaper toward her and her quill pen seemed to echo her indignation as it squeaked across the page. She folded the letter and stepped into the hall.

"Josephine!"

Josephine, startled by the tone of voice, appeared at the head of the stairs.

"Please order the carriage at once and take this note to Mr. Senior. I am asking him to call on me tomorrow."

Miss Ahmansson was a wise companion. She asked no questions. All through tea Jenny was stiff and unbending, but late that night, from the adjoining bedroom, Josephine thought she heard a sob.

Mr. Senior called promptly at nine o'clock the following morning. He was tall and thin, with graying hair, but the sharpness of his features was modified by the warmth of kind gray eyes. He looked at Jenny with fatherly concern as she sank wearily into a chair by the grate.

"Is anything wrong, Miss Lind?" He took the armchair opposite.

"Something very wrong. I promised Claudius—Captain Harris—to ask your advice. As you know, we had planned to be married after my final appearance for Mr. Lumley."

Mr. Senior said nothing, but his very silence was attentive. In slow, halting sentences Jenny told him what had happened.

"What advice do you need?" he asked.

Jenny was taken aback. "Why, about Mr. Lumley. I am torn between my promise to my manager and my loyalty to Captain Harris. And I am asking your advice about another matter, too."

She held up the folded piece of paper. "Captain Harris has written down a few of his suggestions about our marriage settlement. I think what he started to say was *requirements*. They are requirements that I cannot meet."

Mr. Senior gave an encouraging smile. "Yes?"

"It is not enough for Claudius," said Jenny bitterly, "that I have told him I intend to retire from the stage. He must have a promise in writing. Furthermore, I must agree never to sing in public, which would prevent my giving concerts to raise money for my scholarships. Claudius says—he dares to say—"

Jenny, looking down at the paper in her hand, swallowed hard. One word, *unscriptural*, seemed to leap out at her. "He insists that it is 'unscriptural' for a woman to control her own money. He wishes it written into the marriage agreement that I turn my entire fortune over to him. I suspect that is his mother's idea."

The lawyer solemnly studied the tips of his fingers. Had Jenny, in her desire to retire from the world into the arms of a protecting husband, perhaps confused love with her need for love? "I must ask you a very personal question," he said reticently. "Are you—well—deeply attached to Captain Harris?"

Jenny hesitated. "Do you find it so hard to understand why we became engaged? He was so good, Mr. Senior, we seemed to have so much in common. We agreed about religion; at least, I thought we did."

"And now?"

The insistence in his voice, the kindness in his face, broke down her defenses.

"I can hardly be converted to a religion in which I already believe, can I?" Her voice rose in indignation. "That is what Captain Harris and his mother seem to expect. They act as though they want me to go down to Bath as some sort of penitent. Their disapproval of the theater casts a slur on my past life—on the art for which I have sacrificed so much, for which I have everything to thank."

"Naturally, as an artist you are offended."

"Yes, but I have not answered your question, Mr. Senior." The color deepened in Jenny's cheeks. "Speaking as a woman, I—I do love Captain Harris very much."

"That makes it harder for me to advise you."

"Please go on."

"You speak of yourself in a dual role, as an artist and a woman. However deeply you may love your husband you will never be able to forget that you are an artist, too."

Jenny looked at him gratefully.

"In retiring from the stage,"—he spoke slowly and deliberately—"you are ending a remarkable career. You will never forgive yourself if you end it with a failure."

"A failure?"

"Yes, the failure to keep your word to Mr. Lumley. It would be most unwise to disappoint him."

Jenny flinched. "I deserved that. Very well, I shall give the performances."

"Also, as your friend and adviser," Mr. Senior went on, "I cannot draw up the marriage settlement that Captain Harris suggests. In my opinion, only a very selfish man would try to exact a promise that you will never sing again."

"I do not believe I could live without singing," she said softly.

"Exactly. As to the money you have earned and will earn, it is your right to say how it shall be spent. If Captain Harris will not agree to these terms, I believe you will be happier not married to him. If he does agree—and he will if he loves you deeply enough—then go ahead."

Abruptly, Jenny rose. She walked over to the window, her back to the room. Mr. Senior respected her silence; this was a struggle she must wage with herself. When she re-returned to her chair, her decision had been made.

"I shall take your advice," she said. "Will you see Captain Harris for me and tell him?"

"With pleasure!" There was an edge to the solicitor's voice, surprising in one so amiable.

"Draw up the marriage settlement as you think it should read," Jenny went on. "Show it to Claudius. If he still wishes to marry me, ask him not to try to see me until after my final opera. I dare not risk another quarrel—"

Mr. Senior rose to leave and took her hand. "I'll put it bluntly, my dear. Something tells me this marriage will not take place. I am going to France next week to join our friends, Mr. and Mrs. Grote. If you should feel in need of comfort, come to us in Paris."

"I may have need to remember that later." Jenny gave

him a wry smile. "But now I cannot allow myself to think about anything except my roles. These last six appearances for Mr. Lumley must be the best of my career."

Eleven years—thirty operas, 677 performances! The final one was given at Her Majesty's Theatre in London, on May 10, 1849. It was a momentous occasion for both audience and star and Jenny had never received a more heart-warming ovation.

Later that night, she sat at her desk in Clairville Cottage. "My last opera presentation," she wrote in her engagement book. Again she could allow herself to think of Captain Harris.

In the meantime, what had he been thinking? If he no longer wished to marry her, what then? She took a candle and started up the stairs. She would have to try to forget him in working for her scholarship fund; that would have to be her goal. But was marriage, the other goal for which she longed, was that to be denied her?

Captain Harris did not leave her long in doubt. The next morning Josephine announced that he was waiting in the drawing room. Jenny hurried down the stairs. In the hallway she paused, then forced herself to walk calmly into the room. The young man seated in the armchair was staring morosely into the fire.

"Good morning, Claudius."

He rose uncertainly, but Jenny motioned him back to his chair. She took the small chair opposite. An embarrassed silence fell between them.

"You have the advantage of me this morning," Jenny said at last. "I do not know your decision. You do know mine."

Keeping her eyes fixed on the fire crackling in the grate, she drew her shawl closer around her. She yearned yet dreaded to hear what Claudius might answer. Suddenly she realized that he was standing over her. He leaned down, put a hand under each of her elbows and lifted her to her feet.

"Jenny," he said humbly, "may I kiss you?"

"You mean—" Jenny was trembling.

"I mean that everything—*everything*—shall be as you wish, if you will only marry me," he answered. "I have been acting like a selfish beast. Mr. Senior made me see that."

They stood for several moments locked in a long embrace. Claudius said nothing more. Jenny was uncomfortably aware that she had nothing to say either.

"Claudius,"—she drew away and looked up into his face—"what I want to tell you can be told only through music. Always it has been that way with me. May I sing for you?"

"If you wish," Claudius replied. "But, first, don't you think we should both sign the marriage settlement? I have the papers with me."

"Later—later," said Jenny gaily.

She took the papers from him and laid them on the piano. She held him firmly by his arms and backed him across the room. She gave him a slight push, enjoying his start of surprise as he sank back into his chair. "What shall I sing for you?"

"It doesn't matter." He spoke as though humoring a child.

"But it does matter," said Jenny. "Now listen carefully."

She glided across the room to the big square piano. With the first notes of her song her features took on a radiant, haunting beauty that her audiences knew so well.

> *"Birdling! why sing in the forest wide?*
> *Say why? Say why?*
> *Call'st thou the Bridegroom or the Bride*
> *And why? And why?"*

"The Bird Song" had long been a favorite with admiring listeners throughout Europe. Thousands had sat spellbound, as the clear, birdlike tones trilled from her throat with the ease of a nightingale lifting its voice to the sky. It was Jenny Lind's unique gift that whatever she sang the song seemed to come from the depths of her heart—and never, she told herself, had her heart been lighter, more at peace, than on this morning.

She began the second stanza:

> *"Birdling! why is thy heart so blest?*
> *Oh, say? Oh, say?*
> *Music o'erflowing from thy breast?*
> *Oh, say? Oh, say?*
> *My heart is full, and yet is light.*
> *My heart is glad in day or night,*
> *Nor know I why I'm singing."*

"Only that is not true for me any longer." She rested her hands lightly on the keyboard. "Once I, too, sang because, like a bird, I only knew I must. Now I know *why* I sing. I sing because I have found my love. Oh, Claudius—"

A suspicious sound from the armchair made Jenny pause. She whirled around on the piano stool. Captain Harris sat with his eyes closed, his head drooped forward, his chin resting on his chest. His mouth was open. His body jerked. He gave a sudden snort. This time the Nightingale's audience had gone to sleep.

For one incredulous moment Jenny looked at him. Then the hurt which she felt as a woman was quickly replaced by her sense of outrage as an artist.

"How—dare—you?" she said through clenched teeth.

Through the dull, undistinguished years that lay ahead of Captain Harris, he never could be quite certain what had happened. He could only remember Jenny, white and stiff as a statue, her words as they fell from tight lips seeming to freeze into drops of ice. She was asking him to leave, never to see her again. At one point Josephine was summoned to bring his hat and stick. His last memory was of Jenny standing by the piano as she tore the marriage settlement into small pieces.

3 §§

What of the Future?

Jenny reached Paris completely exhausted after the ordeal through which she had passed. She took rooms in the same pension where Mr. Senior and the Grotes were staying, but for several days she kept to her bed, seeing no one but Josephine. Though she knew her friends were deeply concerned about her, she could not bring herself to confide in them—not just yet. There was only one person to whom she felt she could speak of what was in her heart, and she wrote a frantic letter to Judge Munthe.

"Again," she said, "the sun of happiness had hardly risen for me before it set. I need a support, a friend from Sweden —you, my guardian. If you really are my friend, I beg you to join me in Paris."

A few days later the judge arrived. Jenny dressed hastily and went to meet him. She threw her arms around his neck, then stepped back to look up into that kind, dignified face with its thick growth of whiskers. The gray eyes behind the steel-rimmed spectacles had a glint of humor in them as he led her over to a sofa and sat down beside her.

"Now, *lilla* Jenny, what went wrong?"

Jenny sighed. "I suppose one trouble was, Claudius was too young, only twenty-three, and he was always telling me what his mother said. She treated him like a child, and kept him on a very tight leash. I feel sure his outrageous demands were her idea, and between the two of them I would have gone out of my senses."

"It is well that you came to your senses," said the Judge drily. "But someday—"

Jenny thought she knew what he was about to say, and she shook her head. "No, I shall never marry, but I see quite clearly there is infinitely much for me to do with my life. From now on I shall wed myself wholly to well-doing."

It was easy to talk to Judge Munthe. Ever since he had become her legal guardian she had turned to him for advice both about her career and her charities. He handled all of her financial affairs, and she was anxious to consult him about her scholarship fund. It was characteristic of Jenny in her time of trouble to seek forgetfulness in thinking of the needy Swedish students she hoped to benefit.

"This is the most ambitious project you have undertaken," the Judge reminded her. "You realize it will require a very large sum of money."

"Yes, but I can earn it by singing in concerts. I already have enough for my own needs, which are simple, and to provide for my parents."

The Judge glanced at her pale face. "Yes, but this concert tour—you must not undertake it until after you have had a long rest."

"Just talking with you has made me feel rested," she insisted, "and now I am eager for you to meet my friends. I fear I have caused them a great deal of worry."

The judge had dinner that same day with Mr. Senior and the Grotes. George Grote, a well-known historian, would be occupied with his writing, but Mrs. Grote was busy with plans for a holiday that would help Jenny to recover from her recent disappointment. Paris was at the peak of Maytime beauty, and the friends took long walks and carriage rides together. With the horse chestnut trees a mass of pink and white blossoms, and the flowerbeds in the Gardens of the Tuileries a medley of color, it was impossible to remain listless and depressed. One evening, as Jenny and her companions returned to their pension through the Tuileries, they heard a nightingale singing.

"Ah, Miss Lind," said Mr. Senior gallantly, "what a wise man it was who first called you 'the Swedish Nightingale.' "

She stood quite still, listening enraptured, as the golden melody poured from the shadows. Suddenly it ceased.

"There, he has seen us. Now that is just like me. I should have done the same if I had caught anyone intruding on my privacy."

The friends walked on through the gathering dusk. Jenny was grateful that they had asked no questions about Captain Harris, but she wanted to reassure them.

"Do not worry about me," she said. "I am once more myself. What happened in London was really for the best. I probably should not have been happy with Captain Harris."

Mrs. Grote exchanged a glance with Mr. Senior. Each sensed the other's relief.

"I shall now think only of my scholarhips," she went on. "If only I can come at all near my aims in this. . . ."

"You will Jenny," Mrs. Grote assured her.

"Then no one is to be more envied than I. All makes at last for good." Jenny spoke firmly, perhaps trying to convince herself that the words were true.

The next morning, in the course of another stroll with Mr. Senior, she led the way down toward a square off the Rue St. Lazare. They entered a turfed courtyard surrounded by a handsome house, and her eyes rested for a moment on the marble stairway. She walked over to the fountain and stood watching the thin stream of water rise into the sunshine.

"How I used to envy that fountain," she said.

Her companion looked at her inquiringly.

"Yes, I envied it, because it was not obliged to sing. I was so miserable in that house, Mr. Senior. It used to be the home of Señor Garcia, the singing master."

She had been twenty-one years old at the time and already a star at the Royal Opera House in Stockholm. As her fame increased she was convinced that she was receiving praise she did not deserve. She needed more training. Her friend, Giovanni Belletti, a baritone with the Opera, had suggested the distinguished Spanish master, Manuel Garcia, who was then in Paris. To earn the money for a year of study, Jenny had made a long concert tour which, in addition to her frequent performances in opera, had strained her voice.

"I shall never forget," she went on, "the first time I climbed those marble steps and asked the master to take me as a pupil. He had me try a few scales first. I was tired and frightened, but I began to feel more confident when he asked me to sing an air from *Lucia di Lammermoor*. It was one of my favorite roles, but on that dreadful day I broke down."

The memory of her despair was still vivid but she forced herself to go on. "Señor Garcia told me quite bluntly that it would be useless to try to teach me. I had no voice left."

"I thought you *had* studied with Garcia," said Mr. Senior.

"Yes. He agreed to give me another trial, if I would promise not to sing, not even speak for six weeks. Those were weeks when I was living on my tears, but I obeyed. When at last I returned to the studio, I had the joy of hearing Señor Garcia say that my voice was much improved."

"He may have saved it by forcing you to rest," Mr. Senior pointed out.

"Yes, and I was enchanted with him as a teacher. I studied with him for nearly a year."

With a final look around the familiar courtyard, Jenny turned to leave. "It was very fortunate for me that there was a Garcia." She spoke softly. "Do you not see what I mean, Mr. Senior, when I say, 'All makes at last for good'?"

Jenny had to remind herelf of those words many times during the next few weeks. Her stay in Paris came to an abrupt end when a cholera epidemic forced her and her friends to flee the city. She parted from them in Belgium. She and Josephine were going on to Germany, and Judge Munthe had to return to Sweden. Before leaving he again warned Jenny that she must not undertake her concert tour too soon.

"Forget all responsibility for a while," he said.

"All right, I'll try."

It wasn't an easy promise to keep. After she left her friends it was more difficult to seem gay and carefree. She was more tired than she had realized—tired, body and soul. Her nerves were shattered, and once she and Josephine had settled down in Germany she was deluged with letters. Some begged her to sing again in opera, which she refused to do. Other offers came to sing in concerts. The letters came from England, from Russia, and even from far-off America, but Jenny was unable to concentrate on any of them.

Finally in Coblenz she went to see a noted doctor. After a thorough examination, he looked at her gravely.

"Fräulein Lind," he said, "your heart is fatigued. Unless you nurse yourself properly, you may break down completely when you take up your work again."

"Herr Doktor, what am I to do?"

"You should settle down in some quiet place and rest. You are not to try to sing for several months."

The words had a familiar sound. At the doctor's suggestion she and Josephine found rooms in a small health resort in the Austrian Tyrol. Day after day she sat on the terrace of her hotel, a rug across her knees, and let the peace of the mountains seep into her soul. She tried not to think of Claudius. Though thankful and relieved that she had broken the engagement, that did not make her pain and humiliation any easier to bear. She tried to substitute other memories.

She saw herself as a thin, plain-looking girl growing up in Stockholm. Thinking back, it seemed that she had sung with every step she took, with every breath she drew. She remembered her father, talented and charming. She recalled her mother, sharp-tongued and irritable from her efforts to earn a living for the little family. Finally Fru Lind had taken a position as governess in another town and Jenny, at the age of eight, was sent to board with an elderly couple. They were the caretakers of the Widows' Home, where her own grandmother, her beloved *Mormor,* lived. The lodge by the gate was the nearest thing to a happy home that she could remember.

Something warm and soft was rubbing against her ankles. It was a kitten, and Jenny took it up into her lap. There had been a cat like this at the Widows' Home. How she had loved that little bunch of purring gray fur with the blue ribbon around its neck! When she sang, it would nestle closer in her arms. One day after her lessons were done, she sat in the window of the caretaker's lodge singing to her pet. In the street below a crowd had gathered.

Among the people who stood listening under the caretaker's window was a young woman who presently hurried down the street, her cape billowing behind her. She was the maid of Mademoiselle Lundberg, a dancer at the Royal Opera House. Breathlessly she reported to her mistress about the *flicka,* the little girl, who sang so divinely.

The dancer's curiosity was piqued, and she wrote to Fru Lind, asking that she bring her daughter to the theater. There Mademoiselle had listened, amazed, as Jenny sang a Swedish folk song. The nine-year-old child was finally brought to the attention of Count Puke, head of the Theatre

School for Girls, who considered her talent so remarkable that she was admitted as a pupil, with all expenses paid. She was to be educated by the state.

The years that followed were filled with incredibly hard work. At seventeen, Jenny was given the leading role in the opera, *Der Freischütz.* Never would she forget her stage fright on the opening night, or the tumult of applause that followed her first performance. The directors of the Royal Opera gave her a handsome pair of silver candlesticks to help her remember the date on which she became famous.

Shortly after this the newspapers dubbed her "the Swedish Nightingale." She sang as naturally as a bird, it was said, and she soon became the idol of all Sweden.

But what of that other Jenny, whose longing for love and affection her unfortunate mother seemed unable or unwilling to satisfy? Even when quite small she had sensed that she was an unwanted child, but not until she was fourteen did she understand the reason. Anne-Marie, her mother, had been divorced before she met Jonas Lind, and for some reason had stubbornly refused to remarry while her first husband still lived. After his death her union with Jonas was made legal, and it came as a shock to Jenny that she had been born out of wedlock. In the Sweden of 1834 this was a serious situation for a sensitive, adolescent girl, and she ran away. For a while she lived at the school, but this refuge was only temporary. The parents took the case to court, and she was forced to return to their home, where she stayed until she was nineteen.

Looking back on those years, Jenny Lind realized that Fru Lind's uncertain disposition had been rooted partly in anxiety. With the anxiety removed she had become calmer, a little more contented, and a better relationship had developed between mother and daughter. Even so, Jenny was troubled by constant pleas from both parents for more money, always more money, and she found it hard to resist.

Yet she knew that her mother's demands were unreasonable, and that her father would spend whatever she gave him on alcohol. In despair she had asked Judge Munthe to handle the matter of financing their needs, a task he had reluctantly assumed for Jenny's sake.

Jenny set the kitten down gently. She would always be grateful to Judge Munthe. She was grateful to many other friends, but friendship had not compensated for the lack of a happy home. Nor had success.

By the end of October, Jenny felt strong enough for the journey to Hamburg, Germany, where she was to give the first of a series of concerts after her long rest. As she stood at her hotel window looking down on a cobbled street, she thought of the time she had stopped here on her way to Paris. Among her traveling companions on that journey, one face stood out—that of Giovanni Belletti. Giovanni had been his gayest and most charming self, helping her to forget for a few days the dreaded interview with Garcia.

Some years later she had returned to Hamburg to sing in opera. The night of her final performance some students had unhitched her horses so they might have the honor of drawing her carriage back to her hotel. Students! She had met one of them again in England, and he had accompanied her in several concerts.

"Josephine," she said, "isn't it here that young Otto Goldschmidt lives?"

Josephine looked up from the trunk she was unpacking. She puckered her forehead as she smoothed the wrinkles from Jenny's white satin. "The one who had studied with Herr Mendelssohn?"

Jenny nodded. "Yes," she went on, "I am sure of it. Herr Goldschmidt told me that his father was a merchant here. We must find out if the young man is at home, Josephine. I would like him to accompany me at some of my concerts. He is a musician of great promise."

The youth who presented himself at the door of Jenny's suite in the hotel a few days later was tall and slender, with a thin, sensitive face. He was obviously ill at ease as he bent over her hand.

"Fräulein Lind," he spoke in German, "I am honored that you remember me."

"I never forget a good accompanist, Herr Goldschmidt."

The young man flushed, pleased by the compliment.

"Nor could I forget—"

The two gazed into each other's eyes. There was no need for words to know that both were thinking of Felix Mendelssohn.

"Nor could I forget you yourself, good brother."

Otto flushed again, this time with annoyance. Jenny was puzzled. In Germany, as in Sweden, it was the custom to call good friends *brother* or *sister*. She corrected herself hastily. "Well, Herr Goldschmidt, shall we try some music together?"

Jenny saw much of young Goldschmidt during the next few weeks. They rehearsed nearly every day and appeared together in several concerts. He even persuaded her to sing some of Herr Mendelssohn's songs, something she had been unable to do since his death. Their memory of their friend whose influence had touched them both was an ever-tightening bond between them.

It seemed entirely natural to confide in Otto. In spite of his youth, he had a depth of understanding which reassured her. To her surprise, she found herself telling him of her plans for her scholarships.

"I have saved enough money for my own needs," she said. "Now my dearest wish is to help the poor children of my own country who have a talent for the stage."

"Then you will return to opera after all."

"Never. That part of my career is over. I shall sing in concerts. I have had a number of good offers."

"These offers, would they take you away from Germany?" he asked hesitantly.

"Yes, of course. I even have been asked to go to America."

"Why not the moon?" Otto's laugh sounded hollow.

Jenny laughed, too. "America is too far away, I suppose, but the idea is appealing: a new, young country with fresh and eager audiences. But the managers who have approached me ask me to take too many risks. Fortunately, better proposals have come from Russia and England."

"And England is close at hand," Otto pointed out.

"Oh, but I could not spend a year in England—not now. . . ."

She paused, dismayed at how close she had come to revealing herself. "I always find it difficult," she went on more slowly, "to have to rely on my own judgment. Still, I have almost decided to make a tour of Russia."

"You would find it very cold there." Otto was thinking of her recent illness. "Would it not be too much for your strength?"

"I am quite well again. Even so, I don't exactly look forward to a Russian winter."

"Then why. . . ."

"Because I must try to get money." The shrug of Jenny's shoulders had an air of finality. "Yes, I think that we shall go to Russia."

4 §§

"I Have Decided to Go to America."

Jenny Lind was racked by indecision. Josephine was ill, and they were staying in a small hotel in the neighboring town of Lübeck. Her condition was not serious, but would she be equal to the strain of a Russian tour—the long distances between towns and cities to be traveled in sub-zero temperatures? As Jenny sat by her friend's bed, Josephine tried to reassure her, but Jenny could not bring herself to write the letter which would commit her to going.

Even in Lübeck, offers continued to come to her. One morning Jenny sat in the hotel parlor talking with Chevalier Wyckoff, who was trying to persuade her to make an American tour under his management.

"America has been in my mind for a long time," she admitted. "You are one of four managers who have been to see me."

"Three others?" Wyckoff scowled. "What can they offer you that I already haven't?"

"Much the same terms that you suggest. A chance to share in the profits—and also in the losses if the tour fails."

"Why should it fail?" he asked. "I managed the American tour of Fanny Ellsner. That was a success."

"Miss Ellsner is a dancer. How do I know that a singer would meet with the same reception?"

"I tell you, Miss Lind, I have toured America," Wyckoff insisted. "I know what the public there likes."

"Then why ask me to share the risk?" Jenny looked at him steadily. "If you are so sure of the result. . . ."

She broke off, as a maid entered carrying a letter on a silver tray. She noticed that it bore a London postmark. With a murmured, "Excuse me, please," she broke the seal.

The engraved letterhead showed a picture of what appeared to be an oriental palace, with spires and minarets and long-arched windows. It was called Iranistan. Jenny walked over to the window where the light was better.

"Ah, Mr. Wyckoff," she told him, "here is still another offer from America. But this impresario is willing to take all the responsibility. He guarantees me a very large sum."

Wyckoff took a small silver box from his pocket and helped himself to a pinch of snuff. "Who is this impresario? Where is he from? New York?"

"He wants me to give some concerts in New York. He lives,"—Jenny glanced at the letterhead—in a place called Bridgeport, Connecticut."

"His name?"

"My letter comes from a man named John Hall Wilton in London. He is acting for an American impresario, a Mr. Barnum. Phineas T. Barnum."

"P.T. Barnum, an impresario? That humbug?"

The word was not familiar to Jenny, but Wyckoff's laugh, loud and unpleasant, made her flinch. "What do you mean?" she asked.

"I mean that he is a mere showman," Wyckoff replied. "In New York he owns the American Museum. Miss Lind, for the sake of making money out of you, this Barnum would not hesitate to put you in a box and exhibit you throughout the country at twenty-five cents a head."

Jenny glanced again at the engraving of Iranistan. Surely a man who had been successful enough to own such a home, could not be a mere adventurer. And yet—

"I assure you, I will not sign a contract with Mr. Barnum," she said, "until I have a chance to investigate his claims. If I find that others agree with you, Mr. Wyckoff, then I shall be no more interested in his proposal than I am in yours."

Chevalier Wyckoff looked nonplused. What he had heard was true, then. The Swedish Nightingale could be very abrupt when displeased. "You mean. . . ."

Jenny rose and held out her hand. "I mean that I thank you for your offer. It does not interest me. Goodby."

Upstairs in Josephine's room, Jenny felt her first enthusiasm returning. If this new proposition was all that it seemed to be, she need not consider the Russian tour. Nor need she go to England. Mr. Wilton had written that Mr. Barnum was willing to guarantee her a thousand dollars a concert. If she sang in one hundred and fifty concerts she could earn $150,000. Moreover, he proposed to pay the expenses of a secretary and a personal companion—Josephine, of course. An orchestra would be assembled in America, but Miss Lind was asked to choose a conductor, who would also act as her accompanist, and a tenor to appear on the program with her.

"But Jenny!" Josephine propped herself up on her elbow and looked at her friend. "What if Herr Wyckoff is right? What if this American is not reliable?"

"I was rather alarmed at first. I still am," Jenny confessed. "But it is possible that Mr. Wyckoff is merely jealous of a man who has made me a better offer."

"But this—this box that he speaks of?" The perplexed expression on Josephine's long, angular face made it appear even longer. "Would this American really try to. . . ."

"Oh, Josephine don't look so solemn," Jenny could not

help laughing. "Exhibit me in a box? That idea is rather far-fetched, don't you think?"

"Perhaps. . . ." Josephine still sounded dubious.

"It will be easy to find out if Mr. Barnum is reliable," Jenny went on more seriously. "In this letter it says that he has bankers in London—Baring Brothers. Mr. Bates of that firm is a friend of mine."

Jenny wrote several letters that afternoon. One went to Joshua Bates, a second to Mr. Wilton. Yes, she was interested in an American tour, but she must be assured on certain points.

First, about her accompanist and orchestra conductor. Her choice was the eminent German-born pianist, composer, and conductor, Jules Benedict, now making England his home. For an assistant artist, instead of the tenor Mr. Barnum had suggested, she preferred a baritone—Signor Belletti. He, too, was in London singing in opera at Her Majesty's Theatre. Jenny asked that Mr. Wilton call on both gentlemen and try to persuade them to go with her to America. She handed the letter to Josephine to read.

"Giovanni Belletti?" Josephine asked. "Don't you think he might prove difficult on a long tour?"

"What do you mean?" Jenny demanded.

"Well—" Josephine stuttered in embarrassment. "I have heard that Signor Belletti was in love with you during those early days at the Royal Opera."

"Nonsense!" said Jenny. "Some fools would have every man in love with me."

The sharp words were no sooner spoken than she was sorry for them. She dropped on her knees beside the bed and buried her face in the comforter. "Oh, Josephine, how can you speak to me of love, after what happened in England? As for Giovanni. . . ."

Jenny's voice, though muffled, was crisp and firm. "You know yourself that he is the best baritone in Europe. Besides, he is an old and loyal friend. I owe him a great deal."

Josephine seemed taken aback by this spirited defense of Belletti. She smiled wisely, as she let her hand rest on the smooth blonde hair.

"Can't you see,"—Jenny looked up into the older woman's understanding eyes—"if I find that Mr. Barnum is a gentleman to be trusted, then this journey to America will earn me enough for my scholarships."

Waiting for a reply to her letters proved harder than Jenny had expected. Belletti wrote that Wilton had called on him in London and made him a handsome offer. He seemed as eager as Jenny herself to go to America. Mr. Benedict was reluctant to leave his family for so long, but finally he agreed. Several more days went by before a letter arrived from Joshua Bates of Baring Brothers.

Was it possible, thought Jenny as she broke the seal, for Mr. Barnum—for any manager—to keep the glittering promises that had been made in his name?

Her smile deepened as she read. Mr. Bates knew Mr. Barnum personally and could vouch for him as a man of honor and integrity. Even if her tour should prove unprofitable, she could count on Barnum to keep his promises. True, he was a showman, a quite remarkable one, but he was no mere adventurer.

"Oh, Josephine, I feel quite relieved." Jenny thrust the letter into her hands. "Read what Mr. Bates has written."

This letter was followed by a call early in January from John Hall Wilton. Jenny, usually so distrustful of her own decisions, did not hesitate. In the presence of only Josephine and the Swedish consul in Lübeck, she read over the final version of the contract Mr. Wilton had prepared. She was to sail for New York in the late summer. Although her profits were to be used to help the children of her native land, she further stipulated that she be allowed to give a certain number of concerts for the benefit of American charities. Among other provisions in the contract, Mr. Barnum agreed to pay her $150,000 for one hundred and fifty concerts. To guarantee this amount, plus the expenses of the tour, he was to deposit the sum of $187,000 with Baring Brothers even before she sailed.

"There, it is done." She smiled up at Mr. Wilton as she laid aside her pen.

John Hall Wilton was jubilant as he placed one copy of the signed contract in his waistcoat pocket.

"I am sailing on the first steamer," he announced, "to carry the good news to Mr. Barnum. He will be most gratified."

P.T. Barnum was indeed gratified when Wilton's steamer docked in New York the following month. He was risking his entire fortune on a singer who, though famous in Europe, was almost unknown in America. Yet his magnificent optimism never deserted him. His first task was to raise $187,000, but the Wall Street bankers to whom he applied for loans were skeptical.

"It is generally believed in Wall Street," he was told, "that your engagement with Jenny Lind will ruin you."

Fortunately Jenny did not suspect the magnitude of the task which her new manager had assumed. Those days in Lübeck were the happiest she had known for months. Josephine was better. Her own life was settled for the next two years. Shortly after Wilton's visit, she decided to celebrate by giving a children's ball. Among the few adult guests invited was young Otto Goldschmidt, who came over from Hamburg.

"Ah, Otto, I have much to tell you," Jenny murmured as he led her through the slow, swinging rhythm of a waltz. She was conscious of how much older he appeared tonight. How distinguished looking for his twenty-one years! "I am not going to Russia after all."

"I am glad, Fräulein."

"I have had a very brilliant offer," she went on. "I shall be able to earn a very large fortune—enough for my scholarships—in one or two years. As you know, I have no greater wish."

"Where are you going?"

His lips were close to her ear, as he swept her past the orchestra. But at that moment the music blared and Jenny did not hear.

"I have lost nothing by giving up the stage," she said happily. "How good Heaven has been to me!"

And to me, thought Otto silently, at least for a short time.

Otto did not try to question her further. Jenny was poetry in motion as she danced, and both seemed content to let the music flow over them. It came to a slow, quivering stop. Still not speaking, they walked toward an alcove off the ballroom to sit out the next dance. Otto disappeared to bring her an ice, then stood looking down at her.

"Now, Fräulein, please," he urged. "I am chafing with impatience."

"You, my kind, gentle Otto—impatient?" Jenny's laugh was so infectious that Otto laughed, too.

"Yes, even I," he said ruefully. "Don't keep me in suspense any longer. This brilliant offer of which you speak— *where* are you going?"

"I thought I told you," said Jenny. "I have decided to go to America!"

To America! Three thousand miles of ocean between them! Otto's eyes were bleak.

Jenny did not seem to notice. "Mr. Barnum has arranged everything so nicely that I should have been wrong to decline his offer. I cannot help looking on this journey to America as a gracious answer to my prayer."

She paused. For the first time it occurred to her that perhaps Otto would have liked to be included in her company. She wished it might have been possible. But she could hardly have chosen such a young man in preference to the older, more experienced Jules Benedict.

"As my assistant artist," she went on, "Mr. Barnum has signed Giovanni Belletti. You may recall meeting him while you were in England."

Otto nodded. He had a distinct memory of Signor Belletti, as he stood in the wings, watching Jenny on the stage. A twinge of jealousy was quickly replaced by a more generous feeling.

"Ah, Fräulein!" Otto took both of Jenny's hands in his. "May your journey be a happy one, your triumph the greatest in your career."

"It is quite an undertaking, I know." Jenny's laughing eyes grew serious. "America is such a big country; it is so far away. I shall have much to conquer."

"You will conquer it," he assured her, "as you have conquered every country, every city, in which you sang."

To himself he added, As you have conquered every heart.

two

Enter Phineas T. Barnum

Jenny Lind as a young woman. Drawn on stone by R. J. Sane, Esq., A.R.A. Published Feb. 16, 1847 by John Mitchell, Publisher to Her Majesty, 30 Old Bond Street. Reproduced from the Collections of the Library of Congress.

Portrait of Jenny Lind by Jean Baptiste August Lenoir at the Metropolitan Opera House.
Courtesy of the Metropolitan Opera Guild, Inc.

5 §§

The Jenny Lind Boat

The "Jenny Lind Boat" was under way. When it was learned that Jenny and her party were to sail on the S. S. *Atlantic*, there had been a rush for reservations. Every American in Europe seemed bent on one idea: to return home as the traveling companion of the Swedish Nightingale.

During the early part of the voyage, few of the passengers had a chance to get acquainted. The third morning a severe gale swept the sea. For several days lightning flashed, the wind roared, breaking billows surged over the decks and nearly everyone on board was seasick.

Jenny was one of the few passengers who was not ill. This was her first long voyage, and the ocean fascinated her in each of its varying moods. The first night out it was a mirror, brilliant with the reflection of stars and moon. The next morning it was a ruffled gray; by afternoon a calm and brilliant blue, gradually blending into tints of rose and gold at sunset. And then the storm! During a lull she went up on deck. She took a long, deep breath, liking the sting of the salt spray on her cheeks.

At that moment a mammoth wave rose out of the sea. Jenny clung to the railing.

"Quick! Let me help you!" A strong hand on her elbow

was propelling her across the slippery deck and through a hatchway.

"Thank you!" Jenny's tone was courteous but formal as she looked up into the face of Max Hjortzberg, her new secretary.

"I must ask you, Fröken Lind, not to go on deck alone in this storm," he said.

His words were respectful enough, but Jenny bristled at his tone. She decided to ignore it.

"Did you look in on Mr. Benedict and Signor Belletti, as I requested?" she asked.

"I did what I could for them. They are still feeling quite ill." Max shrugged his narrow shoulders. Then as a polite afterthought: "And Fröken Ahmansson?"

"Poor Josephine! She is staying close to her bed. I am going down to our stateroom now."

"Please, will you talk to me for a few minutes?" Max sounded more conciliatory. "I have been trying to see you alone all day."

"Very well."

As they descended the grand staircase, Jenny looked at Max Hjortzberg, at a loss to understand her uneasiness. This young Swede knew English, which would be an advantage. Though Jenny felt at home in both German and French, she had learned English only three years earlier on her first trip to England. Jules Benedict had assured her that, in spite of a slight accent, she spoke clearly and was easily understood. Sometimes she had to pause to find the exact phrase to express her meaning, but Max never seemed to be at a loss for words, no matter what language he used. He was efficient, certainly. Too efficient, perhaps, too domineering. When they reached the commodious writing room, Jenny seated herself in the chair that he held for her.

"Why did you wish to see me, Herr Hjortzberg?"

Max drew up another chair. He wasted no words. "About your contract with this P. T. Barnum."

"You may see the contract, if you wish. But you will have to wait until Josephine feels well enough to unpack our trunks."

"In the meantime, will you answer one question for me? Is there any clause in your contract that might permit you to cancel it?"

Jenny was startled. "Why should I want to cancel?"

"Because," Max paced his words slowly, "as your secretary I feel it is my duty to protect your interests. One of the Americans on board tells me that Barnum is the proprietor of the American Museum."

"I know that." Jenny recalled with dismay that Chevalier Wyckoff had mentioned the museum.

"Herr Barnum coins money out of it, I believe that is the American phrase," Max continued. "Some of the exhibits are educational. Others are in the worst possible taste: horrible monsters recreated in wax, stuffed snakes, skeletons of two-headed calves; bearded ladies and other freaks of nature. If he should have the imprudence to ask you to appear in his museum. . . ."

As his voice droned on, Jenny recalled Wyckoff's words: ". . . this Barnum would not hesitate to put you in a box and exhibit you throughout the country at twenty-five cents a head."

She forced herself to listen to what Max was saying: "Did you know how he got his start in show business? He exhibited an aged Negro woman, representing her as the nurse of George Washington. He said that she was 161 years old, but medical men said she was only half that age. Herr Barnum claimed that he himself had been hoodwinked, but it seems unlikely."

The secretary's smooth clipped voice seemed to reflect a gruesome pleasure in his narrative. Jenny rose.

"Please, Herr Hjortzberg, I do not care to hear any more," she said. "I intend to fulfill the terms of my contract. That is all that need concern you."

Max nodded, trying not to show his anger. He had spoken too soon. This unexpected position as secretary to a famous prima donna had been a piece of good luck and he intended to improve on the opportunity when the time came. Why shouldn't a fellow Swede become her manager? Now he bowed and offered to escort Jenny to her stateroom.

"Thank you, no," she said stiffly. "I feel the need of some fresh air."

Yes, she wanted to let a good clean wind sweep over her. She wanted to let it sweep away her doubts. Just because she did not like Max did not mean that he might not be telling the truth. But what would Mr. Barnum expect of her? What could she expect of him? Ignoring her secretary's warning, she went back on deck. The waves still rose and fell, but less violently, and the sight of the water soothed and calmed her.

The next morning she felt sure of herself again, felt certain of the rightness of this voyage to America. The storm had lifted by the time she awoke. Through the porthole she could see that it was a clear bright day. Josephine was moving about the cabin, her old reliable self again. After breakfast Jenny joined her fellow artists, Mr. Benedict and Signor Belletti, on deck. Both looked fully recovered.

"Ah, Mr. Benedict, and you, Giovanni!" Jenny held out a hand to each of them. "How good it is to be all together again. Why don't we take a turn around the deck?"

Walking between the two men, Jenny glanced from one to the other. Tall, blond Jules Benedict, sixteen years her senior, was always poised and calm. Giovanni Belletti, in some ways, was quite the opposite. His eyes were brown, in a handsome Italian face. His swift temper was as easily placated as it was aroused. Jules seemed like an elder brother, Giovanni like a younger one. Actually he was older than Jenny, but there were times when he acted more like a boy than that young Otto Goldschmidt.

For a moment she considered telling the two men about her conversation with Max Hjortzberg, but decided against it. It would be unkind to burden them with her doubts.

"It does seem so strange to be going to America," she said aloud. "I would never have attempted such a big undertaking without your help."

"We were eager to come," Benedict assured her.

"*Si*. I especially," Belletti added. "Two years ago your recommendation secured me my first London engagement. And now this one. We both stand in your debt."

Jenny looked distressed. "There are no debts between friends," she said. "But if we must speak of them, have you forgotten, Giovanni, how you helped me overcome my stage fright the night I made my debut?"

"I had made my own debut in Stockholm only a month before. I understood."

Jenny smiled at him fondly, then turned to speak with another passenger. Her companions exchanged amused glances. They suspected that it was not just the calm seas and the gentle breezes which had brought so many promenaders on deck.

"The triumph of a nightingale," Giovanni continued in a bantering tone. "You are the admiration, the envy, of everyone aboard this vessel."

Jenny's smile froze. "That is ridiculous," she said. "They have no idea of the incredible difficulties, the heartbreak—"

"The public never does," Jules Benedict reminded her. "Most people think that a triumph just happens."

"Triumph! Loneliness would be a better word. Oh, don't think I am not grateful. It touches me deeply that people are so kind. But few suspect how little the world and its splendor mean to me."

Belletti raised his eyebrows.

"I am not exaggerating when I say that," she insisted. "My wants are very simple. Herring and potatoes, a clean wooden chair and a wooden spoon to eat milk soup with—these things would make me skip like a child for joy."

"I know, *cara mia*." Belletti's voice was suddenly tender. "Yet I still say that I am right. There is not a woman on board who would not change places with you if she could. Not a man who would not . . ."

At that moment they turned a corner and came face to face with a stout lady wearing a red-plumed hat. She clung to the arm of her husband. A little girl about seven held to her free hand. The couple bowed. Jenny returned the bow graciously, but tried to avoid the look of longing in the woman's eyes. Probaby another person who would like to sing!

Jenny turned to Belletti. "You may be right about the passengers," she admitted. "But there are others on board who have a truer sense of values—the members of the crew."

"Shall we find out?" he asked.

"At the first opportunity." Jenny flung his challenge back with a confident smile.

The next morning the three friends visited the engine-room, a part of the vessel few passengers ever saw. Steam-driven vessels for the Atlantic crossing were still something of a novelty, and Jenny was fascinated as she watched the throbbing engines. Any embarrassment the sailors and fire-men may have felt in the presence of their famous passenger vanished in the warmth of her interest.

Benedict and Belletti listened in amazement. In less than an hour, Jenny had learned what each man's duties were. Some volunteered information about their wages, others told her about their homes, their families. One old seaman boasted of his grandchildren and a fireman confided that he was almost sick with worry because of his wife's illness.

The heat in the engine room was intense. Jenny's two

companions mopped their faces with their handkerchiefs, but if she was warm, she did not show it. She was chatting with another fireman, a tall Irishman with hair as red as the flames in the furnace he had been stoking.

"Mr. Benedict, Signor Belletti and I have been having a friendly argument," she told the fireman. "Perhaps you can settle it for us."

"I will if I can, ma'm."

"If you had it in your power, would you be willing to change places with me?"

"Faith, that I would," he said.

Jenny had not expected such a prompt answer.

"I'm lackin' a voice," he added, "but shure an' if I could sing as well, I wouldn't mind at all, at all."

"But why?" Jenny persisted.

"Because the wages are better."

Jenny made a mock curtsy to her friends. Then she held out her hand to the Irishman. "You have lost me my argument," she told him.

By the time Jenny reached the upper deck, her face had become serious. "Those poor men!" she said. "They work so hard and for such long hours in all kinds of weather. Some of them risked their lives for us in the storm."

She turned to Jules Benedict. "What about the pianoforte that Mr. Barnum sent for our use on shipboard? Is it a good one?"

"Excellent," he replied with a knowing smile.

"I see you have guessed what I am about to suggest," said Jenny. "Let us find Captain West and ask his permission to give a benefit concert for the crew."

Captain West was delighted at the idea of a benefit, as were the passengers when they learned of the plan. They subscribed seventy pounds, the equivalent of several hundred American dollars; to this fund Jenny and her two assistant artists made generous donations. They set to work to rehearse the program.

When the day of the concert dawned, fog covered the ocean like a thick gray shroud. After several hours, when it failed to lift, Captain West sent Miss Lind his regrets. He and his officers, responsible for the safety of the ship, would be unable to attend.

By concert time that evening, the *Atlantic* was in the grip of another storm. The passengers had to grope their way to seats in the dining salon.

The opening number was a duet by Jules Benedict and another pianist, a fellow passenger. Their hands could be seen moving over the keys, but the wind was a difficult competitor. It howled outside the portholes. The glass tumblers on the tables kept up a constant jingling, monotonous and out of tune. The floor dipped and swayed. At the end of the number, Benedict rose and bowed. The audience clapped, admiring his composure, but it was not to hear a pianist that they had come. They were waiting for Jenny Lind.

The applause grew louder when she appeared leaning on the arm of Belletti. Even the elements seemed bent on hearing their duet. There was a fortunate lull in the storm, as Belletti's baritone blended with Jenny's bell-like soprano. The audience sat spellbound; but during the next number, a solo by Belletti, they grew restless. He had a rich resonant voice, but again everyone was waiting. When Jenny came forward to sing her first solo, the dining salon rocked with applause.

Jenny sang several times that evening. Her clear pure tones pierced the roar of the thunder, sounded above the crashing sea, and reached to the farthest corner of the crowded room. For her final number she chose a Norwegian folk tune, "The Echo Song." She sat down at the pianoforte to play her own accompaniment.

"*Come hither, come hither, my pretty herd!*
Hu ah! hu ah! hu ah! hu ah! hu ah!"

The last words were an imitation of the herdsman calling to his flock on a mountainside. Jenny turned her face toward the audience, as though listening for the echo of her words. And the echo came, a thin thread of sound, incomparably sweet: "*Hu ah! hu ah! hu ah. . . .*"

The sound of clapping hands mingled with the noises of the storm. When the audience finally let Jenny go, she made her way to a secluded corner of the dining salon. A few palms screened it from the rest of the room, and she sank down on a chair. It was then she saw Belletti.

"Oh, I didn't know you were here," she said. "Didn't the concert go well, in spite of the storm?"

"I suppose so."

Jenny was too tired to notice his aggrieved tone. She leaned back and closed her eyes.

"My only disappointment," she went on, "is that Captain West could not attend. I would like to give another concert for him and his officers, if you and Mr. Benedict—"

She broke off abruptly. For the first time she saw the anger smouldering in his face. "Why, Giovanni, what is wrong?

He shrugged his shoulders. "Could you not see for yourself? When Jenny Lind is on a program, no other performer counts."

"But you were encored, too," she pointed out. "The audience was quite impressed."

"You mean the audience was polite," he corrected her.

Jenny was wavering between irritation at his childish behavior and genuine concern for his disappointment.

"Why do you think I wanted you to come on this American tour?" she asked. "Because you are the best baritone in Europe. Everyone knows that."

He reached for her hand and held it to his cheek. "Ah, *carissima*," he said humbly, "I have been acting very ungrateful."

"You have been acting very foolish." She tried to withdraw her hand, but he clasped it tighter.

"Foolish and jealous," he admitted. "Yet I knew how it would be when I agreed to come."

"You told me that you wanted to come."

"I did! I wanted it more than anything in the world when I learned that you were free. The chance to see you every day—"

"*No!*"

Jenny wrenched her hand away. She had not taken Josephine's suggestion seriously that Giovanni had once been in love with her. For years she had considered him a very good friend. That he thought of himself as something more came as a shock.

"Now that you are free—" he lingered over the words— "there is no longer any reason for me to keep silent."

"But you must. I never dreamed—"

"I know that," he said miserably. "When I first knew you in Stockholm, you were so young, almost a *bambina*. Then we were separated by our travels. When I saw you again, you had become a woman—and you were betrothed to Herr Gunther. Later, when we met in London, it was that English fellow—"

Jenny made a quick little gesture. "You must not ever talk to me of—"

She could not say the word. He said it for her. "Of love?"

She nodded. "I—I was very ill after what happened in England. I cannot let myself be torn to pieces like that again. Now, especially, when I must save my strength for this American tour. That is just as true for you, Giovanni."

"I had hoped that we might find strength in each other,"

he said. "You have often spoken of your loneliness. I am lonely, too."

Jenny pressed her hands against her temples. "You must not—I beg you not to—speak of this again."

She heard footsteps approaching. Max Hjortzberg stood in the opening between two palms.

"Come in, Max." Jenny welcomed the interruption. "I have a message for Captain West. Please tell him we regret that he and his officers could not come tonight. If he would like for us to give another concert—"

She turned to her assistant artist. He seemed to be trying to pull himself together.

"A splendid idea!" he said dully.

The next day was clear, and the second concert was given that evening. To Jenny's relief Benedict and Belletti also received prolonged applause.

After the concert the chairs were pushed back against the wall for dancing. Jenny danced with several of the passengers before Giovanni claimed her. His eyes were lonely and remorseful, but his smile reassured her that he would not bring up the subject which had proved so painful the night before.

"When we sailed," she said, "looking ahead to eleven days at sea seemed a good deal, but the time has passed very quickly."

"*Si*, on Sunday we dock in New York," said Belletti. "Less than three days from now."

Jenny's throat felt tight. Yes, on Sunday, September 1, she would meet Mr. Barnum.

6 §§

Welcome to America

Sunday morning, at the suggestion of Captain West, Jenny climbed the narrow steps to the top of a deckhouse which had been erected over the forward companionway. Chairs had been placed here for the members of her party, and she seated herself between Jules Benedict and Giovanni Belletti.

"There it is at last! The New World!" cried Belletti, as the first faint outline of land showed in the distance. He seemed to relish the drama of the words, almost as if he had rehearsed them.

Everyone was standing now. A gun was fired in salute from the long curving arm of land called Sandy Hook. The salute was answered by a roar from the guns of the *Atlantic* and the ship began to cut its way through the Narrows, the strait between Staten Island and Long Island. The mist, which lay white and fleecy like scattered wisps of cloud on the water, suddenly cleared.

Jenny looked to the north, where sharply silhouetted against the sky the church spires rose above the buildings of New York City. Closer at hand were the boats, filled with people shouting a welcome. Sharp staccato whistles blended with the low eerie call of foghorns. The entire harbor was a blare of sound.

As though wishing to add to the noise, the *Atlantic* fired another salute. The throbbing of the engines was stilled; the paddles ceased to turn; the tide bore the vessel forward. A small rowboat could be seen putting out from Staten Island, and Captain West ordered a rope ladder to be let down.

Two men clambered aboard. One was a health officer for the port of New York. The other was a gentleman elegantly attired in striped morning trousers and a frock coat. During his precarious climb up the ladder, he had some difficulty holding on to his high silk hat. For safekeeping a large bouquet had been tucked into the front of his white waistcoat. He shook hands with the captain, who led the way to the deckhouse.

"Miss Lind," said Captain West, "may I present—"

Jenny was face to face with Phineas T. Barnum.

He was younger than she had expected, a heavyset man of about forty. He was taller, too, at least six feet. She looked up into the big square face; into blue eyes glinting with humor. Reassured, she held out her hand.

"Welcome to America, Miss Lind." He bowed and presented his bouquet.

"Thank you. The flowers are beautiful. Everything is beautiful. This New York harbor is the most"—she was groping for the correct English word—"the most magnificent I have ever seen."

"Except the Bay of Naples," Mr. Barnum replied.

"Not even excepting that." Jenny smiled. "But I am curious, Mr. Barnum. When did you hear me sing? Was it in London?"

"I have never had the pleasure of seeing you before in my life."

Jenny could hardly believe that she had understood him correctly. She was remembering the large sum on deposit in a London bank.

"How is it possible," she asked, "that you dared risk so much on a singer you had never heard?"

"I risked it on your reputation, ma'am. That was enough for me."

He did not add that he had been as much influenced by Jenny's good works as by her accomplishments as a musician. Every cent he had been able to raise had been invested in this venture. For it to succeed, he knew that it would not be enough merely to interest "the fashionables." Thousands of Americans who had never attended a concert before must be induced to buy tickets. To arouse their interest, he had frankly traded on Jenny's reputation for benevolence. He gave no hint of how he had been preparing the public for the day of her arrival.

For months the suspense had been mounting. American newspapers had printed column after column about her fabulous career, her triumphs, her friendship with the great of Europe. And always they mentioned her goodness, her kindness of heart. It would seem that Jenny Lind shared many attributes in common with the angels. Only she had the added attraction of glamour.

Some of the articles were written by a London music critic who attended the concerts Jenny gave in Liverpool shortly before she sailed, and his enthusiastic reviews were sent across the Atlantic on the fastest steamer. Other articles were by Mr. Barnum himself. In one letter to a New York newspaper, he maintained that he would bring the Swedish Nightingale to the United States, even if he knew that he would not make a penny out of the enterprise.

So anxious am I—he asserted—*that this country shall be visited by a lady whose vocal powers have never been approached by any other human being, and whose character is charity, simplicity, and goodness personified.*

Fortunately, he thought, glancing down at the demure figure who stood beside him, she lived up to the publicity. She wasn't beautiful. The pale, honey-colored hair, coiled in a thick bun over each ear, showed glints of gold under her light blue bonnet, but her features were plain. Or were they? Each swift change of feeling was reflected on her mobile features, as the panorama of the New York skyline unfolded before her.

Not only the harbor but the two dark rivers, which hemmed New York in on either side, were filled with hundreds of boats of all kinds and sizes. Within a few minutes the *Atlantic* was gliding past the big round building known as Castle Garden, near the southern tip of the city. Her secretary called her attention to a schooner anchored offshore. It flew a Swedish flag. Her face clouded, but the moment of homesickness was quickly over. She turned back to Mr. Barnum.

By now the ship was nosing its way up the Hudson River toward its dock at the foot of Canal Street. Above the whistles and the foghorns, people could be heard shouting. People! Every small boat was filled with them, waving hats and handkerchiefs. Men, women, children, thousands of them, peered down from the roofs of buildings and leaned from the windows.

"Is this a holiday, Mr. Barnum?" Jenny asked. "There is such a large crowd."

"It has gathered to welcome you, Miss Lind."

"That is kind of them. But how could they know I was coming? I mean, how could they know that our ship would dock today?"

Her manager wisely said nothing.

"And everyone is so well dressed," she exclaimed. "Have you no poor people in this country, Mr. Barnum?"

Before he could answer, there was a commotion on a sloop tied up near the berth of the *Atlantic*. One of the passengers had climbed on the railing. In his anxiety to get a closer look at Jenny Lind, he lost his balance. There was a mighty splash as he fell overboard.

"The poor man!" Jenny clutched Mr. Barnum's arm. "Why doesn't somebody help him?"

"Never fear. Somebody will."

Even as he spoke, she saw a policeman kneeling on the wharf and holding out a long pole. The man in the water grasped it. A minute later, wet and bedraggled, he was pulled to safety.

"Why, the young scamp!" Mr. Barnum roared. "Instead of a view of the nightingale, he got himself a cold duck!"

Jenny was puzzled. She seemed to be saying Mr. Barnum's words over to herself, perhaps translating them into Swedish. When she realized the meaning of his pun, she laughed. A little shakily. But she laughed.

"Miss Lind." She heard a familiar voice at her other elbow. "May I have the honor of escorting you to your carriage?"

Gratefully, she took Captain West's arm. The gangplank had been hoisted on board and covered with a red carpet. Two lines of police were formed to provide a passage from the foot of the gangplank to a waiting carriage.

The dock had been transformed into a bower of green trees, ornamented with flags in her honor. Two triumphal arches, under which she must pass, were decorated with evergreens and flowers. One bore the inscription *Welcome, Jenny Lind*. The other, in tall letters under the figure of an American eagle, proclaimed *Welcome to America*.

All eyes were on her: a slender girl in a long broadcloth cloak and a lace-trimmed bonnet hesitating at the top of the gangplank. "Welcome, Jenny Lind!" someone shouted. Someone else took up the cry. The dock, the buildings and houses, the ships in the river, rang with her name.

Jenny felt her confidence return. These were the people for whom she had come to sing. Mr. Barnum sensed the change that came over her. The crowd sensed it, too. Even at a distance they seemed to feel the magnetism of her presence. Another cheer rose from the docks.

Jenny nodded to Captain West. Her fingers tightened on his arm as they walked down the gangplank. Behind them walked her manager, acutely conscious of his new dignity as an impresario. He took off his high silk hat and waved to the crowd. It wouldn't matter, he thought jubilantly, if his star had the voice of a crow. Her voice was only one facet of a luminous personality.

Master of exaggeration Barnum might be. But in that moment he knew that he had not exaggerated Jenny Lind.

7 §§

An Amazing New World

Jenny heard a clock strike midnight. Ten hours since she had arrived in the New World! She had intended to write to her parents immediately, but until now she had not had a minute to herself. Lying back on the sofa in her luxurious sitting room at Irving House, she began to compose a letter in her mind.

"I have met with the most astonishing reception," she would say.

"Exhausting" would be a better word. She was bone tired; even her toes and fingers ached. In the adjoining bedroom Josephine was unpacking. From below her windows came the low hum of conversation. Jenny was reminded of her admirers in the English provinces who had gathered outside her hotel to chant:

"Jenny Lind O! Jenny Lind O!
Come to the window!"

But this American crowd was much larger. There must be thousands waiting in the densely packed street. Even at this late hour they stayed on, hoping for another glimpse of her.

From the moment she disembarked, there had been no letup in the excitement. The ride from the docks in a carriage drawn by four horses, the press of human beings, the police trying to hold them back, the horses moving inch by inch, the driver brandishing his whip. She hoped that no one had been hurt.

Again and again Jenny had bowed and waved, acknowledging the cheers of the crowd. Benedict and Belletti, seated opposite her, received a scant share of the attention. Not so Mr. Barnum! He sat on the high seat beside the driver, obviously enjoying the ride.

Jenny was of two minds about her new manager. At dinner he had engaged her in an amazing conversation. He made it clear that the American public admired her not only for her talent but for what he called her angelic qualities.

"The folks around here," he said, "would certainly go for it if—"

At this point, he had given her an appraising glance out of shrewd blue eyes. What would she think, he asked, of having him rig up a system of hidden pulleys? It would then be possible for her to descend to the stage from above.

Jenny stared at him in disbelief. It did not seem possible that Mr. Barnum had said what she thought she had heard. How could she have given the impression she would ever consider such a plan? In her confusion she lapsed into her native Swedish, but hastily corrected herself.

"I—I mean you cannot be serious," she said.

Barnum's hearty chuckle, the shrug of his big shoulders, intimated that the idea had merely been one of his jokes.

"You'll have to get used to me, Miss Lind," he said. "I'm quite a wag."

The next minute he had deftly changed the subject. The regular price of admission to her concerts would be three dollars, but he planned to offer the choice seats at a public auction. These would go to the highest bidders, and the ensuing excitement would be good advertising.

Jenny had made no reply. She always preferred that admission prices to her concerts be kept as low as possible, but as she recalled the conversation she was glad she had raised no objections. After all, her manager was risking huge sums. The decision was rightfully his.

Jenny snuggled deeper into the cushions of the sofa. For several minutes she had been only vaguely aware of the sound of music in the distance. Gradually it grew louder, blending with the murmurs of the crowd. Then she heard a knock, a brisk rapping of the knuckles that already she had learned to recognize. She sat up and smoothed her hair. Josephine came from the bedroom to open the door to Mr. Barnum.

"Miss Lind, a band is on its way to serenade you," he announced. "They are members of the Musical Fund Society. For three weeks they have been rehearsing in preparation for this night."

Repressing a yawn, Jenny allowed him to lead her to the window. Several hundred torches, carried by as many firemen, revealed a picturesque scene. The roofs of the surrounding buildings were covered with men and boys; others had climbed lampposts or perched on awnings to get a better view. Broadway was jammed. Carriages, in which well-dressed women rode, wound their way in and out among the pedestrians. The firemen, their shirts looking now red, now black, in the wavering light of the torches, forced a passage through what appeared to be a solid mass of human beings. With some difficulty they cleared a space for the band.

"We want Jenny Lind! We want Jenny Lind!" The chant grew louder, more demanding.

Mr. Barnum opened the long window and Jenny, throwing a crimson shawl over her head, stepped out on the balcony. Torchlight mingling with moonlight cast broad masses of shadow on the scene, but some of those thousands of upturned faces she could see quite distinctly. Her pulses quickened as the band began its serenade. The first number was short, and she felt disappointed that it should be over so soon.

"Oh!" she exclaimed, and joined in the applause.

Later in the program, Mr. Barnum leaned over the railing and asked the band to play "Yankee Doodle." Jenny was puzzled by the word *Yankee* until Mr. Barnum explained that it was a nickname for people of the United States, especially those from New England. What he did not add was that he was considered a typical Yankee, shrewd, industrious, and with a talent for what he called "money getting." Jenny, fascinated by the rollicking tune played by the band, unconsciously beat time with her foot.

The next number was a surprise, for the serenade ended with the music of "God Save the Queen." Her face lighted when Mr. Barnum explained that the same tune served for an American hymn:

> "*My country, 'tis of thee,*
> *Sweet land of liberty. . . .*"

"How beautiful! How splendid!" she exclaimed. Then, with another glance at the red shirts in the crowd below, she added, "The Americans, they are all firemens?"

Mr. Barnum repressed a smile at her quaint English. "Yes," he said, "on fire with musical enthusiasm."

Jenny stifled another yawn. The Americans were certainly on fire with enthusiasm, musical or otherwise. Her only wish now was that they would let her go to bed.

But this was not to be. When she turned back to her sitting room, she found a committee from the Musical Fund Society waiting to see her. She smiled valiantly as their spokesman, a Mr. Watson, began a long prepared speech.

"Mademoiselle Lind," he said, "the welcome we tender

you is by no means sectional. We are Americans—Swedes, Germans, Italians, French and English. But whether we come from the sunny South, the icy North, or the bounteous West, our welcome comes equally from the heart. . . ."

As the grandiloquent phrases rolled on and on, Jenny grew more uneasy. These Americans expected so much of her. Could she possibly live up to their expectations?

Fortunately she did not know that the same thought was troubling Mr. Barnum. Had he advertised Miss Lind too thoroughly? Six months before, most of the mob who welcomed her with such gusto had never heard her name. He had deliberately set out to whet their curiosity, but he had not counted on public interest reaching such fantastic heights. There was grave danger the first concert might prove an anticlimax.

Whatever Mr. Barnum's secret worries, he did not wear them on his sleeve. He was his usual hearty self on Monday morning when he called for Jenny Lind at Irving House. Benedict and Belletti were waiting in her sitting room, and the four of them set off together to select a concert hall. Although it was raining, a bevy of new admirers surrounded the carriage each time it paused. Nor was Jenny's heavy veil much protection from hundreds of staring eyes.

And yet it was a pleasant drive. Mr. Barnum was proud of the city, and he wanted his visitors from abroad to see Fifth Avenue, lined with handsome brick mansions faced with brown sandstone. In 1850 New York was many times smaller than now, thinning out into a mere scattering of houses north of Thirty-Fourth Street. Farms hugged the rivers. What was later to become Central Park was still a wilderness, but the lower part of Manhattan was already a cosmopolitan city.

The skies were beginning to clear by the time the carriage rolled past Bowling Green Park. Mr. Barnum's smile broadened as his driver turned again into Broadway. This was the most bewildering street of all. Lumbering stage-coaches and omnibuses, horse-drawn streetcars, and hackney cabs created a traffic problem even then.

Although rubbish clogged the gutters, no one seemed to notice. There was too much else to see. Bright-colored posters hung on wooden crossbeams or pillars outside the numerous shops and proclaimed the bargains to be found inside.

With a loud "Whoa!" the driver drew up before a large, four-story building at the corner of Vesey Street. The walls were covered with huge paintings of exotic birds, wild beasts and reptiles, and a bizarre collection of human beings. These included a bearded lady, an impossibly thin man, a few giants and General Tom Thumb, the debonair midget Mr. Barnum had exhibited in both Europe and America.

"There it is, folks!" said Barnum. "The American Museum. The ladder by which I climbed to fortune."

His three guests leaned forward to peer at the bizarre-looking building. Mr. Barnum had sent his agents to all parts of the world to find curiosities for his museum. He had exhibited a rhinoceros and grizzly bears and the first hippopotamus ever seen in America. He had brought bands of Indians from the American frontier to perform their war dances. These were only a few of dozens of attractions which the public could see for a quarter, the amazing owner went on to explain. In addition, each night he presented what he called "a moral drama" in the lecture room.

Lecture room! The three musicians exchanged glances. Would they be expected to give any concerts there? Jenny shuddered. The picture of the bearded lady seemed bigger each time she looked at it.

With his next remark, Mr. Barnum relieved her mind.

"There will not be time today," he said regretfully, "to visit the museum. There are several concert halls I wish you to see. I know you want to get the matter settled."

Something seemed to be wrong with each of the auditoriums they inspected. In some the acoustics were poor. Others were too small. The last stop was on the Battery, a fashionable promenade skirting the water at the southern tip of the city. A bridge led to what was then an island, with a narrow strip of water between it and the mainland. On this island stood the large circular building Jenny had first seen from the deck of the *Atlantic*. Castle Garden, Mr. Barnum explained, had once been a famous fort. Now it was a place of amusement, the largest in New York.

When they entered, Jenny stood on the stage and looked out at tier after tier of seats, rising in the balcony to a ceiling of almost incredible height. She wondered if her voice could possibly fill such a vast place, but when she and Belletti tried a few bars from one of their duets, they found the acoustics excellent.

Mr. Barnum seemed pleased by their approval. Castle Garden could accommodate seven thousand persons, possibly more. He would have the stage extended ten feet, over the pit where the orchestra ordinarily sat. The soloist would stand there and thus be closer to the audience. The orchestra would be seated back of her on the stage.

On Jenny's return to Irving House, she opened the door of her suite to find her elegant sitting room looking like a shop. A rather untidy one! Cloaks and bonnets, fresh from their wrappings, were strewn about on chairs. A blue gown was draped across the back of the sofa. Josephine hurried to clear off a chair for Jenny.

"They're presents, Jenny!" Josephine's gesture took in the littered room. "Most of them are from shopkeepers. All they ask is that you acknowledge them over your signature."

Max Hjortzberg, sorting a mountain of mail, was not so agreeable. He had divided the letters into three neat piles, one much higher than the others.

"Are all those letters for me?" asked Jenny.

"Yes, Fröken Lind, and most of them are pleas for charity." With his quill pen, Max indicated the tallest pile of mail. "Herr Barnum has done a thorough piece of work in advertising you as Lady Bountiful. Everyone who needs money expects you to supply it."

It had been a tiring day, but Jenny made an effort to control her temper. Again she wondered if she had made a mistake in her choice of a secretary. The constant attention to detail required of him was bound to prove irksome to a highstrung, impatient young man.

"I am sorry there are so many letters to be answered," she said. "Please consider each one carefully. Select the requests that seem most worthy, and send a small donation in my name. To the others, write as kind a letter as you can. But now you must both listen while I tell you about this morning. Mr. Barnum is taking Castle Garden for our first concerts. He says it will seat more than seven thousand people."

"Seven thousand?" Max threw down his pen and strode across the room to face Jenny.

"Fröken Lind, I cannot keep silent any longer," he said. "Herr Barnum is cheating you outrageously. If seven thousand people hear you at a single concert, can you not see how much money he will make?"

Jenny was silent; the same thought had occurred to her. A thousand dollars for each concert had seemed quite generous when she signed the contract, but she had not known that she would sing before such immense audiences.

"If Mr. Barnum wants to hold me to my contract," she replied, "he has a legal right. But I intend to speak to him about it tomorrow."

The next day, when P.T. Barnum called, Jenny sat at her desk, the contract before her. She came at once to the point.

Her manager listened attentively, wondering if Max Hjortzberg was back of her request. That young man had managerial ambitions himself, Barnum suspected. But no matter! He picked up the contract.

"Miss Lind, this is the document which you signed in Germany, is it not?"

"Yes, and if you insist I am ready to abide by it."

"Please." He handed the contract back to her. "Be so good as to destroy it. Have your lawyer prepare another. You decide what I should pay you, and I will sign."

"Why, Mr. Barnum!" Jenny rose and grasped his hand. "It is just as Mr. Bates told me. You are indeed a man of honor. You are being very liberal."

"Why not?" he asked. "The ticket sales are going better than anyone expected. I figure there will be enough money in this enterprise for all of us."

Barnum's smile was bland. He knew it was good business to keep Jenny satisfied. Besides, hadn't he intended to suggest such a change anyway?

8 §§

"The Manager and the Nightingale"

According to the new contract, Jenny and her manager were to divide the net profits from the tour. Mr. Barnum was to pay all expenses and guarantee her a minimum of one thousand dollars for each concert. The contract covered one hundred and fifty concerts as before.

Jenny, looking ahead to a long hard season, asked for another provision. After her one hundredth performance, she was to have the privilege of withdrawing if she wished. In return, she would pay a forfeit of $25,000.

Another clause stated that she could terminate the engagement at the end of the sixtieth performance. In that event she must refund all sums in excess of a thousand dollars a concert. Both parties knew this clause would probably not be invoked except in an emergency.

"The way things look now"—Mr. Barnum did some rapid calculations on a piece of paper—"your share of the proceeds from the first concert should come to ten thousand dollars."

It was hard to believe. "That is so much more than I expected," said Jenny impulsively, "that I would like to give it all to charity. I mean to New York charities."

"Bless my eyes! That's most generous of you," said Barnum. Her casual offer was exactly what he needed to confirm the impression he had been building up about his star.

"Not at all." Jenny disliked being praised for her charities. "I am only giving in proportion to my gains. Can you let me have a list of worthy institutions?"

"Why not consult the mayor?" he suggested. "It would be good. . . ."

He had started to say "good advertising" but checked himself. "I mean that Mayor Woodhull would welcome the opportunity to advise us."

The first concert was announced for Wednesday evening, September 11. Meanwhile the Jenny Lind "mania" threatened to get out of hand. The street in front of her hotel was thronged with the curious, not only New Yorkers but visitors from outlying towns. Every incoming steamboat and railroad train carried passengers whose sole purpose was to see the Swedish Nightingale.

Whatever she did was reported in the press. Newspapers devoted column after column to her comings and goings. The auction sale of tickets for the first concert, held on a rainy Saturday in Castle Garden, was attended by four thousand people. The auctioneer announced that he was standing on the exact spot where Mademoiselle Lind was to sing. The first ticket went to the highest bidder for $225.00.

"It is amazing," Jenny said when she read the news item later, "what heaps of money people have here!"

Hastily she laid the newspaper aside. Must it always be the same? Praise in the newspapers. Shouts from the crowds, endless compliments from her visitors.

Even from Mayor Woodhull. The day he called to welcome her officially to the city, he was well launched on a prepared speech when Jenny interrupted.

"You frighten me," she said. "Everybody frightens me with too much praise."

The mayor bowed. 'We think you are worthy of it. You, the queen of song—"

"Please!" Jenny interrupted again, then went on in her precise English. "I fear I shall not come up to your expectations. If you continue to flatter me in this way, I shall tremble when I come to sing."

Jules Benedict was having his problems, too. His first task was to assemble an orchestra for the Castle Garden concerts. Joseph Burke, an excellent violinist, was to be concert master, and Benedict was pleased with the other musicians selected. He was not so pleased about the words of a poem he had been asked to set to music. Several weeks before their arrival, Mr. Barnum, in one of his shrewd publicity schemes, had offered a prize of two hundred dollars for the best "Greeting to America" for Jenny to sing at her opening concert.

The contributions had poured in, most of them very trite and banal. A committee had weeded out all but six of the poems, and from these Benedict had chosen the one he thought most adaptable to music. Even so, he had found the words dull and uninspiring. Finally, with the manuscript in his hand, he walked down the corridor to Jenny's suite.

He found Giovanni Belletti there, too, his eyes sparkling with fun. Certainly a change for the better, Benedict reflected, for the Italian baritone had been rather sulky of late. There had been little chance for him to see Jenny alone, and no one else had paid much attention to him. He would gladly have shared in the limelight which Jenny shunned.

"Ah, Jules, I am glad you have come." Belletti seemed about to explode with enthusiasm. "I am about to show Jenny *Barnum's Parnassus.*" He took a small book from his pocket. "It is a parody on his prize contest. I do not understand all of the queer American words, but some of the songs are very funny."

Benedict shrugged his shoulders. "What I have to show is not—funny. I have finished the music for Mr. Barnum's prize ode. Very uninspired music, I regret to say."

Jenny held out her hand for the manuscript. "Perhaps it is better than you think, Mr. Benedict."

The first line was all right: "I greet with full heart the Land of the West. . . ." The next hardly fitted her concept of the United States as a republic. She frowned slightly as she read:

> *"Whose Banner of Stars o'er the world is unrolled;*
> *Whose empire o'ershadows Atlantic's wide breast. . . ."*

Humming a few bars under her breath, Jenny beat time with her fingers on the arm of her chair.

"I like the music better than the words," she said, and all three burst out laughing at her faint praise. "Now may we see your book, Giovanni?"

She leafed through the pamphlet which contained eleven witty parodies of the songs submitted in the prize contest. She paused to read one entitled "The Manager and the Nightingale."

"Listen to this," she said gaily.

> *"I'm a famous Cantatrice, and my name it is Miss Jenny,*
> *And I've come to these United Unites to turn an honest*
> *penny.*
> *Says Barnum, 'If you'll cross to the mighty Yankee na-*
> *tion,*
> *We can make in that Republic a royal speculation.*
> *Just resign yourself to me, and we will raise the wind,*
> *As sure as my name's Barnum and yours is Jenny*
> *Lind.'"*

The friends, even though they did not understand some of the colloquialisms, were carried along by the amusing rhythm.

"This next stanza," Jenny explained, "is supposed to be Mr. Barnum speaking."

Her voice deepened in imitation of her manager's booming bass:

> " *'So, Jenny, come along! you're just the card for me,*
> *And quit these kings and queens for the country of the free;*
> *They'll welcome you with speeches and serenades and rockets;*
> *And you will touch their hearts, and I will touch their pockets;*
> *And if between us both, the public isn't skinned,*
> *Why, my name isn't Barnum, nor your name Jenny Lind!'* "

Jenny laid the book down, puzzled as she often was by American expressions.

"Skinned?" she asked. "What does it mean, *the public isn't skinned?*"

"Another of our manager's jokes, I suppose," said Jules Benedict drily.

The *Parnassus* was one piece of advertising that had not cost Barnum a cent, and he enjoyed the parodies as much as anyone. What did it matter if they poked fun at him? Any publicity was welcome if it made people talk.

And talk they did! Special permits were required to attend rehearsals, but with or without permits many New Yorkers managed to get inside Castle Garden, so they could boast they had been among the first to hear the Swedish Nightingale.

On the day before the opening concert Jenny was singing the "Casta Diva," when her voice was drowned out by
the sound of firing. She paused, then began again, only to
be silenced a second time by the guns on Governor's Island
nearby. There was no use trying after that. She waited patiently, as one blast followed another in quick succession.
Only after silence was restored could Mr. Barnum explain.

"That salute of a hundred guns," he said, "was in honor
of California. It has just been admitted as a state—the thirty-first state in our Union. The United States now reaches
three thousand miles across the continent, all the way from
the Atlantic to the Pacific."

Jenny was impressed. No country in Europe, unless it
was Russia, was so large. That this should have happened
just before her first concert, seemed a good sign.

Mr. Barnum agreed and crossed his fingers.

The first concert on Wednesday, September 11, was
scheduled for eight o'clock, but the doors of Castle Garden
were opened at five. Long before that, the Battery was
thronged with people. For three hours a steady stream of
carriages crawled across the long, well-lighted bridge that
led from the mainland. The waters of the bay were dotted
with small boats, whose owners were doing a thriving business. There were a few men so the rumor went, who had
paid as high as twenty dollars each for the privilege of sitting in a rowboat where they hoped to hear a few stray
notes of music.

Castle Garden blazed with lights. Both parquet and balcony had been divided into three parts, each set off from
the other two by lamps of a different color. The middle
part of the house was yellow, the left red, the right blue.
The ushers in the different sections carried wands ornamented with gay knots of ribbon in the same three colors.

There was no confusion as seven thousand people were
shown to their seats, so well had Mr. Barnum planned. Yet

the air was electric with anticipation. Promptly at eight o'clock, the sixty-piece orchestra took their places on the stage. The applause was hearty but tinged with impatience. As the lights dimmed many in the audience stole another hasty glance at their programs. The overture would be followed by a baritone solo. Not until after that would they hear Jenny Lind.

Backstage, Jenny was seated at her dressing table. She was wearing white, with low-cut bodice and a graceful full silk skirt in the fashion of the day. It was a beautiful dress, but the eyes that looked back at her from the mirror were hollow and sick. Stage fright was not new to her. Before every public appearance for the past twelve years she had gone through the same devastating sensation, but tonight the tension which had been building up in her was almost unbearable. She knew that an audience with hopes keyed too high was the hardest to please.

Besides, Max had given her some disturbing news. The evening's receipts fell more than two thousand dollars short of the original estimate. The reason, according to Mr. Barnum, was that many of the tickets sold at the auction had never been called for. They had not been paid for. Max was suspicious of this explanation. But Jenny had been in no mood to discuss her manager's honesty—or lack of it.

She was thinking that her share of the proceeds would be less than ten thousand dollars. And she had promised to donate ten thousand to local charities. How could she keep her word?

In the distance the low hum of conversation gave place to an unexpected hush. Jenny sensed the impatience. Seven thousand people were waiting, waiting to judge her. She hid her face in her cold fingers.

Josephine laid a reassuring hand on her shoulder. "Come, Jenny, you cannot go on with your eyes red from weeping. See, I have the white rose for your hair."

Jenny ran a powder puff over her face. The silence out front was broken by the tuning of instruments. She could almost see the flourish of Benedict's baton, as the strains of the overture to the opera *Oberon* were wafted faintly backstage.

Jenny inclined her head to listen. It was a good orchestra. Belletti, who came next, was in excellent voice; but she hardly heard the end of his solo. Then there was a knock on her dressing-room door. Time for her to go on; the moment had come.

For the audience, it was a moment of breathless suspense. Several thousand people swayed forward in their seats, their eyes on the tall girl with the white rose in her hair. She moved with slow grace, as Benedict led her toward the footlights. Her curtsy, with white skirts spreading around her, had all the beauty of an arrested movement in a dance. It was a gesture of gratitude, of modesty, even humility.

In a single involuntary movement, the audience rose to its feet. They waved their handkerchiefs and tossed hats in the air. Their cheers shook the building.

Jenny struggled to keep the tears back. She had been given ovations before, but never one like this. Never had she sung before so many people. The mass of faces seemed to merge into one giant face, the hall to revolve in a whirling circle of colored lights.

With quiet finally restored, the conductor raised his baton. Jenny braced herself, took a deep breath, and began the "Casta Diva," her favorite aria from the opera *Norma*.

"Casta Diva, Casta Diva. . . ."

Her voice faltered, the notes tremulous and uncertain. A sigh of disappointment, felt rather than heard, rippled through the auditorium. Jenny's face blanched. Josephine, watching from the wings, was afraid that she would break down. Belletti, who stood beside Josephine, clenched his hands. Mr. Barnum took out his handkerchief and wiped the perspiration from his florid face.

The change came suddenly. It was as though the sound of her voice held magic for her, as it usually did for others. Jenny forgot herself in her music. Again she was Norma, druid priestess of the forest, a part she had played many times on the operatic stage. Her face took on a strange arresting beauty, as she prayed to the Queen of Heaven for aid. Her tones rang out, pure and true, and though she sang in Italian, the meaning of her words was impressed on every heart:

> *"With thy quiet, oh bless us,*
> *Let thy peace shine on our night,*
> *Oh, shine on our night."*

Jenny was entirely herself again; the audience was completely her captive. For a high soprano, she had a remarkable range. She combined sweetness with power, but her listeners were stirred not so much by the voice as by the woman herself. By sharing with them her own depth of feeling, she made them conscious of depths in themselves which they had not known existed. Their emotions found release in applause, even while the last golden notes lingered on the air. They pelted the stage with flowers.

Cries of *Bravo! Bravo! Jenny Lind!* shook the high rafters of Castle Garden and sounded over the waters of the bay.

The three who stood in the wings were caught up in the excitement. The staid Josephine threw her arms around Belletti's neck. Mr. Barnum beamed. He had risked an enormous sum on a hunch. The hunch had paid off.

In all Castle Garden, only Jenny Lind seemed to remain calm. The last vestige of stage fright was gone. She felt a fresh surge of gratitude as she stood under the white and gold proscenium arch, her arms filled with flowers. She curtsied and tried to leave the stage. Again and again she was called back.

That the audience should grow more enthusiastic with each succeeding number would have seemed impossible, and yet it did. The "Greeting to America" at the end of the program brought more cries of Bravo! People were shouting themselves hoarse. Jenny thought that they would never let her go.

She was seated at her dressing table, weak with fatigue, when Mr. Barnum knocked on her door.

She smiled up at him. "What a joy it is to see the people so satisfied!" she said. "But I am troubled about the receipts, Mr. Barnum. Max told me they fell short."

Mr. Barnum gulped, not prepared for her abrupt change in mood. One minute she was the "angel" he had been advertising, the next a practical woman of business.

"That is true," he said, "but I have a suggestion. Would you be willing not to count tonight's concert or the one you will give day after tomorrow in our regular contract? If we divide the net proceeds from these first two concerts, you will have more than enough to make your donation."

"I could not wish for anything better."

Out beyond the footlights, thousands of voices were joined in a new cry; "Where's Barnum? We want Barnum!"

The big man shifted his weight from one foot to the other. "I am really very reluctant to respond—"

"Oh, but the people want you. You must not disappoint them," Jenny assured him earnestly.

For one so "reluctant," Mr. Barnum fairly sprinted toward the stage. Jenny stepped into the wings to listen to his speech.

"Ladies and gentlemen," he began, "I have but one favor to ask of you. That is, in the presence of that angel—"

He pointed to the door through which Jenny had recently passed. The rest of the sentence was drowned in a roar of approval. Jenny turned and hurried back to her dressing room. She refused to listen to another word of praise.

"Josephine," she said, "please order the carriage. We must leave here before the crowd does. I hope, oh, I hope, that we can slip into the hotel unnoticed."

Meanwhile on the stage, Barnum was holding up his hand for silence.

"Yes," he repeated, "in the presence of that angel, I ask to be allowed to sink where I really belong—into utter insignificance. If there has ever been a moment when I aspired to have the question generally asked, 'Where is Barnum?' that time has passed forever. You must acknowledge that after such a display as we have had tonight, Barnum is nowhere!

"But, my friends, I beg leave to tell you where Jenny Lind is. Her portion of the profits tonight will be in the neighborhood of ten thousand dollars, and she had declared —"

Barnum paused. His timing was perfect. The sound of seven thousand people breathing seemed temporarily suspended.

"Miss Lind has declared," he went on, "that she will not receive one penny of her part of proceeds of the concert. She—will—devote every bit of it to charitable purposes. It will be disposed of as follows."

He read the list of institutions and organizations to be benefited. At the end the audience called again for Jenny Lind.

There was no response. She was safely stowed away in her carriage, driving through a strangely quiet city.

"Oh, Josephine," she said sleepily, "isn't it beautiful that I can sing so?"

9 §§

The Lind Fever

The next day Mr. Barnum was besieged with offers.

"I dare say there are at least a hundred men in New York who would gladly pay me two hundred thousand dollars for my contract," he boasted to his new assistant, Le Grand Smith. "But, by thunder, I wouldn't sell it for a million."

Jenny was scheduled to go on to Boston after four more concerts in Castle Garden. Le Grand was to leave at once to make arrangements and hold an auction for the sale of the first tickets. He was a friendly, industrious young man whose help was sorely needed. Although Mr. Barnum was never one to soft pedal his own achievements, no one but he himself realized how much hard work had gone into his preparations.

Jenny looked forward to Boston, hoping to find it a quieter city. Meanwhile in New York the "Lind fever" showed no signs of abating. Any number of articles bearing her name—gloves, bonnets, pianos, chairs, sofas, even cigars and sausages—were offered for sale. Poems were written in her honor; songs dedicated to her. Hundreds of young ladies imitated her hairdress. Jenny was amused until she learned of a rumor that was going the rounds. Could it be, one newspaper asked, that Miss Lind wore her hair about the ears because she had no ears? She flushed angrily as she tossed the newspaper across the desk to Mr. Barnum.

He read it placidly, glad that he had brought along some letters which might distract her. Like Jenny, Barnum had an accumulation of mail asking for charity. Luckily a few of the letters were amusing, and he hastily leafed through the pile. One note summed up the writer's problem in five words:

god Nose I am Poore.

The spelling in the second letter was perhaps even more original. A needy gentleman had written:

I tak grait pleshur in Readin' my bibel, speshily the Proffits.

"And for sheer nerve," Barnum showed her a third letter, "this one takes the cake."

But Jenny failed to see anything humorous about the plea of a Pittsburgh woman who had recently become the mother of twins. She had named the girl Jenny Lind, the boy Phineas T. Barnum. In gratitude for this favor, Mr. Barnum was asked to provide for their future education and support; for their immediate needs, the mother informed him, she would need five thousand dollars.

Without a word, Jenny gave this extraordinary communication back to him. She glanced at the pile of unanswered mail on the desk. Max had given up in despair trying to reply to each request.

"If only the newspapers would not always publish a list of my charities, I might not receive so many letters," she complained. "I hope the newspapers won't find out about tomorrow."

Mr. Barnum said nothing, but he listened attentively when Jenny spoke of her plan to visit the New York Asylum for the Blind. This visit would also be well publicized, but Jenny was still unaware of that, when she arrived at the institution. More than one hundred and fifty students had assembled in the chapel, and she seated herself at the piano to play her own accompaniment. Many of the sightless young people in her audience were studying music, and they were so carried away by their enthusiasm that it wasn't enough for them just to applaud. After each number they shouted their approval, and Jenny felt well repaid for the time she had taken from her busy schedule.

Later, on her tour of the building, she was surrounded by students who reached out to touch her. They wanted to "see" her, they said, and seemed to think that a great joke. When one pretty girl, about sixteen, hung back shyly, Jenny went over and put an arm around her shoulders.

"Can't you see at all?" she asked.

The girl's face brightened. "No, but when you sing hearing is a greater blessing."

Back in her hotel, Jenny's sitting room was filled with callers. One of the hardest problems she had to cope with was the constant stream of visitors. No sooner would one leave than another, sometimes many others, would demand her attention. A number of them made blunt appeals for cash. Jenny was so tired, so pressed for time, that usually she would give a small sum to anyone who asked.

"Is that all?" One indignant woman thrust a twenty-dollar bill back into her hands. "I scarcely expected that you would offer such a pittance. I had heard that you were generous. But I see, Madame, that I was sadly mistaken in your character."

Jenny closed her lips tightly, then coolly turned her back and began talking to another caller.

She could not bear much more, she was thinking. She was grateful to New Yorkers for the warmth of their welcome, but she would be glad to move on to Boston. Bostonians, she had been told, were more dignified.

Great was her surprise, therefore, when she arrived at the

Boston railroad station on a damp Wednesday morning in late September, to find a large crowd waiting in the rain. Another throng gathered in front of Revere House. This hotel, recently built, had been named in honor of the American patriot, Paul Revere, and Jenny longed to relax before the fire in her attractive sitting room. But the crowd outside was calling her name. When she appeared at the window to acknowledge their cheers, she looked down on a forest of umbrellas.

"Oh, Josephine, I wish it would stop raining," she said pettishly. "All of those people down there will probably take cold. Why should they want to come out in this weather? To look at me. I am sure"—with a shrug—"there is not much to see."

She herself felt the beginning of a cold and she drew her chair closer to the fire. At that moment Le Grand Smith was announced. When he saw her tired face he realized that he had come at an unfortunate time. At least he could be glad that he had good news to report.

"Miss Lind," he said, after he was comfortably seated on the other side of the grate, "the results of the auction are even better than in New York. The first ticket went to a singer and entertainer by the name of Ossian F. Dodge. The price he paid"—Le Grand paused impressively—"was $625.00."

Jenny, not too familiar with American currency, did some quick mental arithmetic. Why, the sum was the equivalent of more than a hundred English guineas.

"What a fool!" she said aloud.

Le Grand wanted to laugh, but the firm line of Jenny's chin made him wonder if he dared.

"Well,"—there was a suggestion of a twinkle in the brown eyes—"one of the Boston newspapers has suggested that since you are called the Swedish Nightingale, Dodge might take the name of the Guinea Fowl."

The tension was broken. Jenny's giggle was like a schoolgirl's. She decided that she was going to like Le Grand Smith.

"I don't believe we need worry about anyone not getting his money's worth," he went on. "Mr. Dodge is an entertainer. He sings comic songs, and when he plays his circuit in New England towns this coming winter, he won't be modest about linking his name to yours. He will undoubtedly net many times the sum he paid for his ticket."

"But how can it help him—to link his name to mine?" asked Jenny plaintively. "How can all these excitements help *my* concerts? I met many curiosity seekers in Europe, of course. But I wasn't torn and bothered from morning to night the way I am here."

"This is a new country, Miss Lind." Le Grand leaned forward in his chair, trying to explain. "You are the first great musician who has visited us at the height of his fame. Except for a few who have traveled in Europe, our people do not even know that they *want* to hear you. So these excitements are necessary."

He hesitated, but Jenny was looking at him earnestly, taking no offense.

"It is Mr. Barnum's task, and mine, to arouse a desire in people to come to your concerts. If our methods seem extraordinary, remember that you more than fulfill the promises we make in your behalf."

He was interrupted by the arrival of Max Hjortzberg, who had just returned from Tremont Temple, where the first concert was to be held.

"There will be a full house tonight," he reported jubilantly. "All of the fashionables will be there. Many others, too. While I was waiting in the box office, a young woman, evidently a servant girl, came in and laid down three dollars for a ticket. 'There goes half a month's wages,' she said, 'but I am going to hear Jenny Lind.' "

The secretary took the incident lightly, but not Jenny.

Castle Garden, where Jenny Lind made her first appearance in America, September 11, 1850. Lithographed and published by N. Currier. Courtesy of The New York Historical Society, New York City.

The Jerry Warringer Mansion, Howard Street, Springfield, Massachusetts. It was from one of these balconies that Jenny Lind sang to the school children of the town. When the house later burned, one of the balconies was saved and it is now in the Connecticut Valley Historical Museum.
Courtesy of the Connecticut Valley Historical Museum.

Jenny Lind cut-out paper dolls, garbed in the costumes of her various operatic roles, with the container box.

Modern Jenny Lind doll, created as a Sesquicentennial tribute to the singer by Madame B. Alexander.

"Poor girl!" she exclaimed. "Would you know her if you saw her again?"

"I believe I would," Max replied.

"Then please watch for her before the concert." Jenny took a twenty-dollar gold piece from her purse. "I would like you to give her this with my best compliments."

She sounded hoarse, and Le Grand looked at her in concern. Her cold was getting worse, and it showed in her voice that night. Even so, her audience was wildly enthusiastic. Reporters who had scorned New Yorkers for their exaggerations began searching their dictionaries for fresh adjectives to describe her singing. Each day after that produced flowery paragraphs about the serenades given in her honor, the torchlight processions, and the spectacular display of fireworks across the street from her hotel.

In Boston Jenny met a number of New England's prominent citizens. Samuel Ward, the Boston representative of Baring Brothers, her London bankers, called with his wife. Mr. Barnum introduced her to a Senator who was staying at Revere House at the time, Daniel Webster. No one needed to tell her that he was one of the greatest living Americans. With his deep-set eyes in his stern dark face, he looked the part. Jenny was overcome with admiration.

"Ah, Mr. Barnum," she said later, "that is a man. I never before have seen such a man."

A very different caller was a mild-looking Harvard professor, better known as a poet. He brought a letter of introduction from Fredrika Bremer, a Swedish author who also was making a tour of the United States.

"Miss Bremer has been telling her American friends of your glorious voice," said Professor Longfellow.

Jenny thought back to a night twelve years before.

"Ah, Fröken Bremer is indeed a good friend. She was present at my debut in Stockholm and was among the first to encourage me."

There were other memories of Fredrika she was less anxious to recall, and Jenny was relieved when the conversation turned to Professor Longfellow's visit to Sweden. He had once spent several weeks in her beautiful northland, he explained, and Jenny found it good to talk of home. Her visitor was fascinated by what he later described as "a kind of soft wildness" in her manner, the "sudden pauses in her speech," and "floating shadows over her face."

A few evenings later she and her friends were guests of the Honorable Edward Everett, former governor of Massachusetts and president of Harvard in the neighboring town of Cambridge. As soon as it was dark, he offered to show them the observatory at the college. At the very instant when Jenny took her place behind the telescope, there was a long flaming trail of light across the sky. Seeing it intensified through the giant lens, she stepped back hastily, her eyes flooded with the brilliance. That meteor, the custodian explained, was the largest and brightest which had been observed for eight or nine years.

"Possibly it may be regarded as an omen," said the Boston *Transcript* the next day, "of the bright reputation which is to attend the great vocalist on her travels through the United States."

"I hope so," said Mr. Barnum fervently, when Le Grand Smith showed him the item.

He was not a man to borrow trouble, but again he crossed his fingers. Was it possible for any human being, even the Swedish Nightingale, *always* to succeed? Would Jenny invariably captivate her listeners? It would seem so. Yet, as he was fond of saying, the public was "a very strange animal," fickle and ofttimes perverse. He could not help wondering what would happen if his star ever had to face a hostile audience. She was so accustomed to praise.

Jenny gave eight concerts in Boston, one of them devoted entirely to sacred music. "To sing oratorio had long been the wish of my heart," she said. "It is the music I love best."

If Mr. Barnum had any doubts about her choice of a program, they were soon set at rest. When Jenny sang "I Know That My Redeemer Liveth," a great surge of emotion swept through the audience.

Despite the grueling schedule in Boston, Jenny came to have a deep affection for the city. She liked the green reaches of the Common, the wide-branched elms, the mellowed brick of the old houses. One afternoon toward the end of her stay, she and Giovanni Belletti went for a drive up the steep slope of Beacon Hill. The horses slowed to a walk, picking their way carefully over the cobblestones.

As the driver guided the horses between the posts that guarded Louisburg Square, Jenny gave a sigh of sheer pleasure. Those tall stately homes, that high iron fence enclosing a scrap of green park in the center, reminded her of London. She and young Otto Goldschmidt had walked together across such a square on their way to a rehearsal. Otto! It had been weeks since she had thought of him. Now she could almost see him, a smile lighting his dark, slim face as he came toward her. Jenny turned to her companion.

"I feel so at home here," she said. "Oh, Giovanni, do you suppose I'll ever have a home, a real home?"

"You could have it, *cara mia*, if only—"

Jenny laid a gloved hand over his. She had not intended to give him an opening to speak.

"Let us talk of something else." Her voice was gentle but firm. "A home could never mean to you what it does to me. The theater is your life."

That was true. He admitted it frankly to himself. But wasn't it Jenny's life, too? Marriage with Captain Harris would have provided the daily round of domestic duties that she seemed to crave. But had she really wanted them?

During the remainder of the drive, he curbed a dozen impetuous speeches. Jenny had a stubborn streak, and to try to force her to a decision might spoil whatever chance he had. He could only wait—and hope.

Doing the States

Jenny's enthusiasm for New England mounted during the railroad journey to Bridgeport, Connecticut, to visit Mr. Barnum. She and her party forgot the discomfort of the jolting coaches in watching the panorama of beauty unfolding outside the train windows. She had never known that October could be like this. The dingy russets and pale yellows which, in the fall, tinted the dying leaves in Europe seemed mute by comparison. There stood a tree glinting like pure gold in the sunlight. Farther on a scarlet maple flamed against a background of dark pines. The hillsides were a tapestry, the sky an azure dome.

The big park which surrounded Iranistan, Mr. Barnum's home, was also blazing with color. The ground was covered with a bright carpet of fallen leaves that crunched pleasantly under Jenny's feet as she stepped from the carriage. She glanced up at the huge three-story palace where her manager lived. Its spires and domes stood out in sharp contrast to the simple white houses of his neighbors. At first glance Iranistan was overpowering.

"I am astonished, Mr. Barnum," said Jenny, "that you should want to leave such a beautiful place to travel through the country with me."

Barnum was obviously pleased as he led her into the house. Built at great cost, Iranistan may have impressed some of his guests as being too ostentatious. A marble stair-case, with statues placed in the niches at intervals in the wall, led to the second floor. The walls of Mr. Barnum's private study were upholstered in brocaded gold satin. The paneled drawing room had paintings of "The Four Seasons" set in the panels. Long mirrors reflected carved divans, rich draperies, and tables inlaid with pearl.

Near the door stood a plain-faced woman who appeared a little out of place against such an ornate background. Be-side her waited her three daughters, ranging in age from three to seventeen.

"This is my treasure of a wife," Mr. Barnum introduced her. "Charity, my dear, this is Miss Lind."

Mrs. Barnum looked up adoringly at her husband, then held out her hand to her famous guest. Caroline, the eldest daughter, stepped forward to be introduced. She had her father's genial smile.

"Mr. Barnum has told me that you will travel with us on our tour," said Jenny. "What a pleasure that will be."

Jenny slept soundly that night and awoke the next morn-ing more refreshed than she had felt since her arrival in America. After breakfast she took Mr. Barnum's arm and suggested a walk through the grounds.

"I have heard the most extraordinary report," she said, "that you and I are to be married. Now how do you sup-pose a rumor like that could have started?"

She sounded half-amused, half-exasperated, but Barnum did not blink an eye.

"Probably from the fact that we are engaged," he replied with a straight face.

"Engaged?" Jenny was puzzled, then remembered that the English word had two meanings.

"I have been thinking about—our engagement," she went on, "and, seriously, Mr. Barnum, there is one aspect of it which is not fair."

Mr. Barnum gave her a keen glance. He hoped that Max Hjortzberg had not been pouring some "silly twaddle" into her ear about changing her contract again.

"My first object is to see you are satisfied," he assured her.

"I know, but people are saying that you contribute nothing when I give a concert for charity. You pay for our travel, the concert halls, the printing of programs and tickets, and much else besides. Yet the newspapers give you none of the credit."

"Bless my eyes, why should they? Fact is, there's a conundrum going around. I have a clipping here in my pocket that I've been intending to show you."

Jenny read it slowly; *"Why is it that Jenny Lind and Barnum will never fall out? Because he is always for-getting, and she is always for-giving."*

The laugh which bubbled up in her throat was quickly checked.

"That is what I mean. It is not fair. You should deduct your expenses before you pay me my share when I sing for charity."

He did not answer at once. He knew that Jenny would not approve if he told her that her reputation for liberality was the best advertising he could hope for. It was better that his own contribution go unnoticed.

The "angel," as his star had been described in numerous press releases, would be more interesting, he reasoned, if there was a villain in the background. And that was a role Mr. Barnum rather enjoyed.

"Mine is a profitable philanthropy," he said aloud. "Cast your bread upon the waters, you know and perhaps it will come back buttered."

Jenny shook her head. She sometimes found it harder to understand Mr. Barnum than Mr. Barnum did to understand her.

From Iranistan the company traveled to Philadelphia for a single appearance, then back to New York. It was a busy time. Besides giving fourteen concerts in three weeks, they must make preparations for the coming tour. "Doing the States," Mr. Barnum called it. Four thousand miles to be traveled. Fifteen cities to be visited. Such a tour would have been unheard of a few years earlier, but the coming of the steam railroad now made it possible for people in cities hundreds of miles apart to hear the Swedish Nightingale. Jules Benedict had already selected a dozen musicians to furnish the nucleus of a permanent orchestra, the number to be increased in some of the larger towns by local talent. Le Grand had two new assistants, Mr. Seaton and Mr. Bushnell.

The tour began with a return engagement in Philadelphia, and from there the company traveled to Baltimore. The residents of both cities had professed to be amused by the antics of Jenny's admirers in Boston and New York, but that was before she arrived. When Jenny stepped out on the balcony that opened off her room in a Baltimore hotel to acknowledge the cheers of the crowd, she dropped her shawl. Immediately it was pounced on and torn into dozens of tiny pieces by souvenir hunters.

One Baltimore lady unwittingly started a rumor that had amusing consequences. She had leaped to the conclusion that Caroline Barnum, whom she had seen riding in a carriage beside her father, was the Swedish Nightingale. On Sunday, when Caroline attended church and sat with a friend who was a member of the choir, this same woman happened to be in the congregation.

"Look!" she whispered to the gentleman on her right. "That's Jenny Lind! She is going to sing in the choir."

The gentleman passed the news on to another. Soon the entire congregation was waiting to hear the first sound of the celebrated voice. Caroline, not realizing she was the object of so much attention, joined in the opening hymn.

"What an exquisite singer!" The church was filled with whispers. "I never heard the like! What heavenly sounds!"

At the end of the service, when Caroline tried to return to her carriage, she found the way blocked. Some time later she rushed into the hotel dining room, her eyes sparkling.

"I couldn't imagine why everyone wanted to see *me!*" she exclaimed. "Then I suddenly realized, Miss Lind—they thought I was *you!*"

"Can you beat that!" her father roared.

"Why, Caroline," said Jenny politely, "I didn't know that you sang."

"I can't. I mean—"

"That's the pith of a joke," Mr. Barnum explained. "We have never discovered that my daughter has any extraordinary claims as a vocalist."

The words were no sooner spoken that he regretted them. Would his prima donna's sense of humor stretch far enough to include a joke on herself? To his relief, she laughed.

Jenny's fame had preceded her to the nation's capital. Le Grand Smith, who had gone on ahead to make arrangements for her concerts, engaged rooms for the party at Willard's Hotel, and on wandering through the public rooms he was gratified to hear no discussion of politics. The question then uppermost in nearly everyone's mind was whether slavery should be permitted in the new territories in the western part of the United States then being opened up for settlement. Washington was the center of the controversy, but all talk on that crisp December afternoon was of the visitor from Sweden.

The day after Jenny's arrival, she went for a drive up Pennsylvania Avenue. Washington, with a population of fifty-one thousand, had many characteristics of a straggling country village. The houses were set wide apart, in contrast to New York, where the buildings seemed to hug one another in order to make room for all. In the capital, there was space and to spare. The broad streets were muddy and many of the small houses were shabby, but the city was beginning to expand along lines of beauty of which its founders had dreamed.

When Jenny returned to Willard's, she was dismayed to learn that she had missed an important caller. During her absence Millard Fillmore, President of the United States, had left his card.

"Come Mr. Barnum," she said, "we must call on the President immediately."

"What's the hurry?" he asked.

"Because he has called on me. That is a command, is it not, for me to go to his house?"

"You can put your mind at ease, Miss Lind," her manager replied. "Tomorrow will be time enough to return the call. Whatever the custom with crowned heads in Europe, our President does not 'command' the movements of strangers."

Jenny did call on President Fillmore the next morning. Later, at his invitation, she, with Benedict and Belletti and Mr. Barnum, spent an evening with him and his family. The three foreigners, accustomed to court etiquette in Europe, were amazed at the informality of the Executive Mansion. Once beyond the high white pillars, they felt as much at home as in a private house.

The hall, built especially for the Lind concerts, was not yet finished. But that did not prevent nearly every famous man in Washington attending the first night. The President and his family were there, as were his Cabinet, several well-known military leaders and practically every member of both houses of Congress. Chairs had been provided for a few dignitaries, but the majority of the audience had to be satisfied with rough wooden benches. The low expectant hum of conversation abruptly ceased when the members of the orchestra took their places.

Jules Benedict raised his baton to conduct the overture, but it was hardly finished when the audience broke into applause. The ovation, though, was not for him. A frail elderly man was slowly advancing down the aisle, and the applause quickened when he finally reached his seat.

"Three cheers for Henry Clay!" came a shout from the gallery.

Henry Clay! Jenny, waiting in her dressing room, remembered the name. It was all very confusing to a foreigner, but according to Mr. Barnum a law pushed through Congress by Senator Clay had averted a disastrous Civil War. At least, that was what many Americans hoped. They considered the Compromise of 1850, the law for which he was primarily responsible, the crowning achievement of a long, distinguished career.

As Jenny advanced toward the footlights, she was curious to see the man who had saved the United States from such a dreadful fate. Though his long narrow face was furrowed with lines of pain, the warmth in his gray-blue eyes made it easy to understand why he had been able to charm so many of his countrymen for more than a third of a century.

Seated close by was another Senator whom Jenny recognized at once. There was no mistaking those heavy brows in that massive dome of a head. It was Daniel Webster. When she finished her solo, he rose in all his majesty, stepped into the aisle and bowed low in the direction of the stage.

Jenny was startled but pleased. She made her deepest curtsy in return. Applause shook the building. Mr. Webster bowed again.

At the second Washington concert, Jenny learned that John Howard Payne was out front. She looked directly at him as she sang:

"Mid pleasures and palaces though we may roam,
Be it ever so humble, there's no place like home."

To the author of that song who, like Jenny, had longed for a home only to have his longing unfulfilled, her courteous gesture brought a happiness he was never to forget. John Howard Payne had spent many years away from his native land and as an actor and a playwright considered himself a failure. He also had been removed from the office of United States Consul in Tunis, but his friend, Senator Webster, was working for his reappointment.

Perhaps it was the Senator who had suggested to Mr. Barnum that Miss Lind sing the song, and when she looked down into that austere face it was working with emotion. Jenny herself was close to tears, and the entire audience had found her rendition a moving experience. From then on she was to include "Home, Sweet Home" in nearly every program.

The day before Jenny Lind left Washington, she visited Mount Vernon. A steamboat was chartered for the short voyage down the Potomac, and at the landing she was met by Colonel Washington, a great-nephew of the general. The colonel's wife led the way through the lovely old mansion, and at the end of the visit she handed the guest of honor a small volume. When Jenny opened it, she found General Washington's name on the flyleaf, written in his own hand. The book had once belonged to him.

Jenny stood silent for a moment, trying to find the exact English words that would express her gratitude. No gift which she had received since coming to America had pleased her so much.

"I shall always deeply value it," she said. "All mankind" —only she pronounced it *mankint*—"loves Washington."

She lingered on the broad *verandah* to take a last look at the curving river. This was the home which Washington had loved more than any spot on earth. He had left it to lead the fight for liberty and many others had risked their lives in the same cause. Yet, she had been told, many

Negroes were slaves. The coachman who drove her carriage in Washington, the elegant waiters in the hotel dining room, many of the dark-skinned people she had seen on the streets, were owned by other men. A country of contradictions—this United States!

The company passed Mount Vernon again the next morning as their boat churned down the Potomac toward Richmond. Two concerts there, and a few days later found them on board an ocean steamer, the *Gladiator*, en route to Charleston, South Carolina. This voyage provided the most frightening episode of the entire tour. The ship ran into a severe storm which lasted for more than a day. When the vessel was not heard from, the news raced along the telegraph wires that it had gone down with all on board. To the seasick, terrified passengers, it seemed impossible that they would ever reach Charleston alive.

Jenny remained calm, at least outwardly. At the end of thirty-six hours, a voyage which usually took less than half that time came to an end in Charleston harbor. By then the weather had cleared. As the carriage wheels rolled through the peaceful streets, she was humming under her breath.

"And so this is Charleston?" Jules Benedict looked about at the tall narrow houses, prim and orderly, their bricks faded with age. "I never thought I'd live to see it."

"Nor I." Belletti was still weary and dejected after his recent bout with seasickness.

"But the storm is over," Jenny reminded him, "and have you forgotten what day this is? This is Christmas Eve."

She remembered the murmuring, snow-draped pines in Sweden, the sleigh ride at daybreak on Christmas morning to attend service at the church, the crunch of ice under her feet, the fading stars in the pale sky as the sun rose to shine on a white world. Here, instead of pines, there were live oaks, festooned with gray moss, and the air of the Southern city was soft and warm.

After their arrival at the hotel, Jenny and Josephine shut themselves up in their suite and worked the rest of the day in secret. That evening, when they threw open the door of their parlor, their guests found a Christmas tree glowing with candlelight. Piled in a mound at the foot of the tree were packages in a variety of shapes and sizes. In addition to the regular gifts, there was a joke for each member of the group. Jenny selected the largest of the packages and handed it to Benedict with an impish smile.

"What have we here?" he asked.

"Open it and see!"

He obeyed a bit warily. Inside the wrapping, he found a smaller package and inside that a still smaller one. Everyone was watching, as he removed endless layers of fancy paper. When he finally came upon a small piece of his favorite tobacco, there were shouts of glee—shouts repeated each time one of the "joke" packages was opened.

Three concerts were given during Christmas week, but Jenny refused to receive callers. She needed rest, she declared, and she was gratified that people in Charleston seemed less demanding than in Northern cities. She and Belletti took long walks along the Battery where the town's most fashionable homes overlooked the water. It was a relief not to be followed, not to have crowds dogging her footsteps.

On New Year's Eve she gave another party in her suite. During the final hours of 1850, Barnum told some of his most amusing stories. The entire company joined in singing the folk songs of their native lands: Sweden, Italy, Germany and America. Finally chairs were pushed back against the wall, and Joseph Burke put aside his violin to play the piano.

"Aren't you going to ask me to dance, Mr. Barnum?" Jenny asked.

"Why, Miss Lind, I've never danced in my life," he replied.

"That's all the better," she said. "Come now, dance with me in a cotillion. I am sure you can do it."

She danced as gracefully as Barnum had expected and he was as awkward as he feared he would be. Jenny was weak from laughing. The third time he stepped on her toes, she led him toward a sofa.

"We'll sit this one out," she said breathlessly. "You are right, Mr. Barnum. I give you credit for being the poorest dancer I ever saw."

Signor Belletti was crossing the room to claim Jenny for the next dance. As he whisked her across the floor, she was still laughing. Her mood changed abruptly when the clock in a neighboring church struck the quarter hour. A quarter to midnight. She walked over to the piano.

"Pray, Mr. Burke, let us have quiet," she said. "In fifteen minutes more 1850 will be gone forever."

She sank down on the sofa, shielding her eyes with her hand. Another year ended! What would 1851 bring? An end to her wanderings perhaps? Time had worked its magic in regard to Claudius. She was able to think of him without pain. Yet the very absence of pain left her feeling empty and more lonely. She was conscious that Belletti was sitting close beside her. He needed to move his hand only a few inches to take hers.

Ah, Giovanni was so devoted! He was so lovable, so much fun, despite an occasional outburst of jealousy. She herself had faults just as grave. She wanted desperately to reach out to him. Instead, she moved her hand away. Why could she not accept what he offered? Could she in time—perhaps during the coming year?

The church clock was striking again. Twelve slow solemn strokes sounded in the quiet night. At the final stroke, din replaced quiet with the sharpness of an explosion. Fireworks clattered, guns boomed, shouts echoed and re-echoed in the street outside the hotel. A hilarious crowd was singing "Auld Lang Syne."

Jenny rose, her smile tender and wistful. One by one she pressed her friends' hands and wished them a Happy New Year.

II §§

Cuban Interlude

From Charleston the party sailed for Havana, Cuba. Jenny, tired of living in hotels, rented a house outside the walls of the city and invited Caroline and Mr. Barnum to be her guests. The first concert was four days off, and she had a chance to relax in the sunshine.

This was Jenny's first visit to a tropical country, and she reveled in the sight of tall palm trees. She liked the tile-roofed houses, with walls tinted in soft blues and greens and yellows. On this happy, sunlit island, she felt more like a carefree child than a famous prima donna.

One day she persuaded her manager, against his better judgment, to play ball with her in the courtyard.

He was panting and his face was red when he returned from retrieving the ball.

"Oh, Mr. Barnum!" Jenny teased. "You let yourself get too fat. You cannot even play ball with me."

She expected him to laugh, but a frown furrowed his usually smooth brow. That was not like him. She wondered what was wrong.

Had it not been Barnum's policy to shield Jenny from worry, he could have told her that the people of Havana were very antagonistic. They resented the high admission prices to the concerts. One newspaper had dubbed him "the

Yankee pirate," but he was determined to charge no less than in the States.

In spite of his forebodings, the ticket sale was better than he had expected. By the time he took his seat in the dress circle on the night of the first concert, he saw that the house was nearly full. But he sensed the hostility in the air. These people who had grudgingly paid the price he asked were waiting in cold silence. The overture by the orchestra was followed by a thin spatter of applause almost more insulting than none at all.

How would Jenny be received? Barnum moistened his lips nervously as Signor Belletti led her toward the footlights.

Jenny appeared frightened, as she invariably did the first time she faced a new audience. But she had never been more beautiful, her manager decided, as she made her usual deep curtsy. She was wearing white, as she so often did, with a white rose in her hair. A few people started to clap but were promptly hissed down. Hisses—for Jenny Lind!

Jenny straightened. Astonishment, fear, outrage were written in quick succession across her mobile features. She stood quite still as she looked out over the audience. They had flung down a challenge. Her eyes flashed defiance as she prepared to meet it. Benedict lifted his baton.

At the first note of Jenny's song, Barnum sensed the surprise of those around him. There was a subdued rustling, an exchange of glances. Some of the proud Spanish aristocrats still kept their teeth clenched, their lips firmly closed. Finally one critic shouted, "Bravo!" It was an involuntary cry, wrung out of him by an overwhelming admiration. The final note brought such a tumult of applause as Barnum had never heard before. He took out his handkerchief and wiped the perspiration from his face.

Jenny had certainly settled them, he thought.

He could see that she was trembling— she who had been so brave and defiant a few minutes before. "Otra vez, otra vez!" the cry sounded through the big hall. Again and again she was called back.

Barnum could sit quietly no longer but rushed through a private box to reach backstage. Jenny was turning back into the wings after her fifth encore when she saw him. She stopped short, amazed at the emotion his face revealed. She threw her arms around his neck.

"Oh, Mr. Barnum, are you satisfied?" she asked brokenly.

"God bless you, Jenny."

For once the voluble showman, "the Yankee pirate," was at a loss for words. How could he have had any qualms about his Nightingale? Whatever the challenge, he knew that she would meet it.

The plan had been to give twelve concerts in Havana. After the harrowing experience of the opening night Mr. Barnum decided to limit the number to four, the final one to be given for charity.

There also was some unexpected competition in the performances of the Havana Opera Company. Señor Salvi, the first tenor of the troupe, when approached by Mr. Barnum, agreed to join the Barnum company. Not right away, but the following April when the season in Havana would be over.

Jenny was pleased when she heard the news. Señor Salvi was an excellent musician. She also looked forward to the holiday which the manager was giving his troupe. Le Grand Smith was sailing at once to arrange for a month of concerts in New Orleans, but the rest of the party would not need to join him until February. After the benefit performance in Havana, they would be free of responsibility for several weeks.

"Mr. Barnum," Jenny said, "I saw you at the gate this morning talking to a crippled man."

"The man with a dog?" asked Barnum. "That was Signor Vivallo, a plate dancer who used to travel with me during my early days as a showman. You should have seen him jug-gle plates as he danced."

"That poor little wizened man could dance? How long has he been lame?"

"Since I last saw him. His left side has become paralyzed. He makes a living, if you can call it that, with his perform-ing dog. His one ambition now is to earn enough money to return to Italy for a last visit with his family."

"Then he must go as soon as possible," said Jenny quickly. "Some of the money earned at my benefit shall be set aside for him. Will you please tell him?"

Mr. Barnum thought of the two hospitals, the convent, and several needy individuals who were to share in the pro-ceeds of that concert. No one person, he was convinced, would receive greater happiness from the benefit than the Italian plate dancer. In this he was right. The day after Vi-vallo learned of Jenny's offer he brought her a basket of fruit.

"I want to thank the good lady," he said. "God bless her! Now I shall see my brothers and sisters again."

"Miss Lind is out driving," Barnum explained. "I shall thank her for you and give her the fruit."

"Ah, no, Signor Barnum." Vivallo was determined to tell of his plan before overcome by the thought of his own boldness. "She pleases me. I want to please her. I bring my dog to do tricks. He can turn a spinning wheel. He can spin very good."

"Now, listen—"

"She is such a good lady," Vivallo interrupted. "I know she like to see my dog perform. Please, may I bring him and the wheel?"

Barnum hesitated. There was no foretelling Jenny's reac-tions, and he was determined that no worries should intrude on her holiday.

"You are quite welcome to the money," he said as gently

as he could, "but Miss Lind does not like to be thanked for favors."

When Jenny returned from her drive, he gave her the fruit but made light of the request.

"You'd never guess," he told her, "how Vivallo proposed to thank you. He wanted to show you his performing dog? Can you beat it!" He stopped abruptly.

"I like that, I like that!" she said. "If it will make the poor man happy to bring his dog, then let him come."

The next day Jenny was waiting at the window long before the little Italian appeared. When she saw him enter the gate, followed by a boy carrying the spinning wheel, she ran downstairs and opened the door.

"It is very kind of you to come with your dog," she told him. The governor of Cuba could not have received a more gracious welcome.

Vivallo was too dazed to reply as a servant helped him up the stairs. Jenny insisted on carrying the wheel, the little dog frisking at her heels. It was a small white poodle, freshly bathed for the great occasion, and he wriggled with pleasure when Jenny dropped to the floor and took him on her lap. As she stroked the silky ears, she looked up at Vivallo, asking many questions. Did he miss his work as a plate dancer? Where in Italy did his family live? Did he plan to stay there or return to Cuba?

Vivallo answered diffidently at first, but his happy Latin temperament soon asserted itself. The dark eyes shone as he put his performing dog through its tricks. Finally the small spinning wheel was set up, and Vivallo took a mouth organ from his pocket. At a command from his master, the dog sat up on its haunches, turning the wheel with his paw, in time to the music.

"I make him spin double queek," said Vivallo.

Faster and faster he played. Faster and faster turned the wheel, until Vivallo took the mouth organ away from his

lips. "The trick—eet is feenish!" he announced triumphantly.

"Bravo! Bravo!" cried Jenny. "Signor Vivallo, I like
your way of saying 'Thank you.' Now it is my turn to say
it. I shall sing you a song."

She seated herself at the pianoforte. As her guest listened,
a smile spreading over the thin features almost erased the
lines of pain. After refreshments had been served, she and
Mr. Barnum stood in the doorway bidding him goodby.

"The sight of his face would repay me for all the labors
of this entire tour," said Barnum. "He has probably never
been so happy before."

"He is no happier than I," she said.

Later that afternoon Jenny went for a drive with Signor
Belletti, who obviously was delighted to have her to himself. He helped her into the *volante*, a strange-looking vehicle, such as neither of them had ever seen before. The
springs of the carriage were suspended between the shafts
of the horses' harness and the two oversized wheels. The
driver, or *Calesero*, impressive in his handsome livery, rode
astride the horse.

"Oh, Giovanni." Instinctively Jenny turned to him to
share her pleasure as the *volante* swung down the Paseo.

This magnificent avenue was bordered on either side by
tall palm trees on which fell the sunlight, hot and golden.
Bougainvillaea vines formed a scarlet tracery on white
walls, beyond which could be glimpsed exotic gardens.
Even the low tile-roofed houses, tinted in pastel shades, reminded Jenny of huge squat blossoms set against a background of green hills.

"Yes, *cara mia?*"

Giovanni took her hand in his. Jenny had never known
him to be so considerate as of late. One could not wish for a
better companion—when they were not singing together.

Why was it so hard, she wondered, to be an artist and a woman, too? Even Claudius, who cared nothing for music, had tried to make her promise never to sing again.

"What is it, Jenny, *carissima?* Of what are you thinking?"

"Of Captain Harris," she replied.

Belletti dropped her hand as though the touch of her fingers burned him. This time Jenny reached out to him.

"Ah, Giovanni, I was thinking that I had *not* thought of him for several months. All at once I realized—"

She lowered her voice, conscious of the nearness of the driver. "I realized that I was free."

"Free to marry me?" he asked exultantly.

"I did not say that."

"But you will," he went on confidently. "I can read it in your eyes."

She turned her face away. "Perhaps, I would, if—if you could always be like this. Oh, Giovanni, why"—she was groping for words—"why must you glare at me after a concert if I happen to get more applause?"

She could feel him stiffen beside her. "How would *you* feel if I always received most of the applause?" he demanded. "You would be angry, too."

"I probably would," she admitted. "That is all the more reason why we must be careful. What if we should marry and then found that we were always quarreling?"

Giovanni shrugged his shoulders. "What would that matter, if we love each other?"

Jenny was silent, remembering her unhappy childhood. Perhaps *her* parents had loved each other, but their shy, sensitive daughter had memories which could make her tremble even now. Her children, if she ever had any, must grow up in a calm and happy home! Giovanni, she suspected, rather enjoyed a good lusty quarrel.

It was nearly dark by the time the *volante* turned in at her own gate. After helping her down, Giovanni held her close for a long moment.

"I shall try not to be jealous of your singing, Jenny," he said humbly. "Knowing myself, I cannot promise. I can only try."

"Please don't urge me," she begged. "We need more time to test ourselves."

"Time?" he asked, thinking back along the years. "How much *more* time do we need?"

"At least, until the tour is over. Perhaps by then I shall know what I really feel. Perhaps we both shall know. But let us not think about it now."

"*Mañana?*" he teased. This favorite expression of the Spanish-speaking Cubans was one to appeal to all Latins. "Tomorrow?"

The other members of the company shared in Jenny's relaxed mood. They took long drives, sometimes pausing to watch slaves at work in the fields of sugar cane. They saw orange groves with golden fruit nestled among green branches. The tropical sun shone on pineapple and banana trees growing by the roadside. Toward the end of their stay, Mr. Barnum arranged for the party to visit a coffee plantation. Jenny's one regret was that Jules Benedict was ill and unable to join in these excursions. But when Jenny visited him at his hotel, he assured her that he was growing stronger every day.

Even Max was in good humor. Late one afternoon Jenny was going over an accumulation of mail with her secretary, when she was interrupted by the arrival of a messenger with a note from Fredrika Bremer, the Swedish novelist. Jenny looked up from the sheet of notepaper, the color rising in her cheeks.

"I did not know that Fröken Bremer planned to visit Havana. It has been years—" She paused uncertainly.

She remembered how Fredrika, a friend of the Lindblads, had blamed her for what happened so long ago. Did she still blame her? Jenny wondered. Why couldn't the older woman have realized that both she and Adolf had tried to do what was right? She felt almost ill, remembering that bitter time, but suddenly she knew how much she wanted to see her old friend.

"Max," she said impulsively, "please order the *volante*. I must call on Fröken Bremer at her hotel."

The novelist had arrived in America eleven months before Jenny. Her travels had taken her from New York to New England, from New England to the South, and as far west as the territories of Wisconsin and Minnesota. She had visited in log cabins of pioneer settlers, in Indian villages, and in the high-columned houses of wealthy Southern planters. When she reached Havana, she was delighted to learn Jenny was still there.

The reunion between the two women was a joyous one. Fredrika kissed Jenny on the cheek, a gesture more eloquent than any words to express what was in her heart. At last she understood, and Jenny needed no other reassurance.

"Ah, *lille* Jenny, to see your face again," Fredrika said in her soft voice. "It has the whole Swedish spring in it."

She fixed her bright eyes on Jenny's face, eager to hear a first-hand account of the remarkable series of triumphs, which she had been among the first to predict. But Jenny did not want to talk about her career. She was more interested in Fröken Bremer. Why had she come to America?

"I wanted to see for myself this rising new world." Fredrika looked much older than her forty-nine years, but there was a lilt in her voice like that of a young girl.

"Strange and wonderful it is the way I have been received," she went on, hardly pausing for breath. "Invitations—requests for autographs—and that everlasting question, 'How do you like America?' I finally began to tell people America was a novel requiring time to read."

"Americans sometimes can be most impatient," Jenny said.

"Yes, but I would be the last to reproach them for their enthusiasm. That is why I like the States. The country is so young, so exuberantly young."

Several times Fredrika had tried to bring the talk back to Jenny Lind.

"Jenny, I am curious," she said at last. "Have all the honors that have come to you, your wealth, your musical reputation—have these struck no root in your soul? Are you really indifferent to them?"

"No," Jenny answered, "I am touched by the good will and kindness shown me, but every day I see around me so many new faces. I yearn for a more tranquil life."

"Of course," Fredrika nodded sympathetically. "It was all in the newspapers, how thousands of people followed you on the street. I said to myself then, 'Ah the poor girl! Hercules himself would not be equal to that.'"

"Jenny Lind isn't either! I intend to end my engagement as quickly as possible, perhaps in a year. Now let us talk of Sweden and old friends!"

The two homesick women spent nearly every waking moment of the next three days together. Under tropical skies they spoke of their far northern land, while Fredrika, an excellent artist as well as writer, made a sketch of Jenny. They took long drives along wide avenues bordered by flowers and palm trees. Fredrika declared herself to be "quite tipsy with the air." Cuba, she said, made her better understand Heaven. But, alas, Cuba had its night as well as its day.

Jenny looked at her inquiringly.

"Slavery is Cuba's night," Fredrika went on, "and that is true in the States, too. Of course, some of the slaves are better fed and better clothed than many Swedish peasants. I visited plantations where the Negroes were kindly treated, but I have no dust in my eyes about slavery. There are evil masters as well as good ones, and to attend an auction where slaves are sold."

She paused, overcome by the stress of her emotion. "Jenny, it rends one's heart. I cannot understand why no one has ever written a novel about this."

"Perhaps you will write one."

"I yearn to." Fredrika warmed to her subject with a story-teller's sure instinct. "I have heard histories of the flight of slaves. They know of no other road to liberty than the road toward the North, following the North Star when it shines by night. During the day they hide in the deep forests. This journey with its dangers and anticipations— ah, what subjects for a novel!"

"Then you will write the book?"

Fredrika shook her head. "No, it is a story that should be written by an American mother. I do not know the country well enough."

That evening she met the members of Jenny's company at supper. Mr. Barnum's funny stories kept them all laughing—all except Max, she noticed. The secretary evidently did not approve of the strange partnership. Certainly no two people could be more different than shy, retiring Jenny and the irrepressible Mr. Barnum.

Fredrika's interest centered on Signor Belletti. He sat beside Jenny, saying little, his eyes eloquent with unspoken love. Jenny's face softened whenever she looked at him, yet she seemed troubled.

The following evening, Jenny's last before she left for

New Oreleans, she and Fredrika went for a final drive. There was a new moon in the sky, flooding the world with its pale magic.

"How like a boat it looks," said Fredrika, "floating on the western horizon."

"Yes, and so different from the moon at home," Jenny added. "Could it be because Cuba is so much farther south than Sweden?"

Fredrika looked at her keenly. "It is not of the moon that you are thinking."

"No, I am thinking of Giovanni. I wish you could advise me, but no one can. Only my own heart can tell me what to do."

Yet she found that it was a help to talk about her problem. She was very fond of Belletti but his jealousy of her as a fellow artist, even though he tried to control it, stood between them. It was a situation she was powerless to prevent, except by giving up her music. Perhaps that was the answer. She had tried to give up love, only to come back to the old conclusion: She could never find real happiness except in home and family.

"Would they be enough for you?" asked Fredrika. "Could you ever forget that you are a great artist?"

Jenny was silent. It was almost the same question that Mr. Senior had asked her two years before.

"It is as you said." The older woman's voice was warm and comforting. "Your own heart will decide. You have made thousands of people happy, Jenny. Whatever happens, may you be happy, too!"

The next day Fredrika was rowed out to the *Falcon*, the ship on which Mr. Barnum's party was to sail. Jenny had already gone aboard. She was pale and depressed as she said goodby. She merely glanced at the big bunch of white roses Fredrika had presented as a parting gift.

It was not until Miss Bremer was seated again in the small

boat which was to take her back to shore that Jenny seemed to come to herself. She touched her lips to one of the roses. She kissed her hand to her friend—a mute expression of gratitude that the cloud of misunderstanding between them had been lifted. The last Fröken Bremer saw of her, she stood leaning against the rail, her cheeks wet with tears, but with her face illumined by the light that was peculiarly Jenny Lind's.

Jenny stood by the railing for a long time. She thought ahead to the fatiguing round of rehearsals and concerts. She thought of Giovanni. Havana's beautiful harbor was slowly fading in the distance. Jenny strained her eyes for a final view of the low varicolored houses, the tall stately palms, and the old fort, Morro Castle, silhouetted against an incredibly blue sky.

What was it Fröken Bremer had called Cuba? "A heavenly oasis between two hemispheres."

For Jenny it had been an oasis in time. And now. . . . *mañana* was almost here.

An Inconsistent Angel

Two days later Jenny stood at the same railing as the S.S. *Falcon* plowed its way into the muddy waters of the Mississippi River. Mr. Barnum who had joined her on deck pointed out a cotton plantation, where gangs of slaves, their backs bent low, were picking the cotton bolls. She could make out quite plainly the slave cabins and, farther on, the home of the owner. It was a gracious white house with a two-story veranda on three sides, supported by tall columns.

"Now we are approaching New Orleans," said Mr. Barnum.

In a curve of the river, shaped at this point like a huge letter *S*, she could see the city, which at first glance seemed to be more of Europe than of America. The faint outlines of the twin-towered cathedral in the distance gave promise of a quiet peaceful town, but a closer view showed New Orleans to be a busier place than any the musicians had yet visited. The broad wharves that stretched along the waterfront for several miles were crowded. As the *Falcon* slid into its berth and deckhands prepared to lower the gangplank, someone spied her standing beside her manager.

A shout went up: "There she is! That's Jenny Lind."

There did not seem to be a vacant inch of space on the entire wharf. The noise, the turmoil, filled Jenny with panic. Already the peaceful interlude in Cuba seemed like a dream.

"Mr. Barnum!" Her voice was sharper than she realized. "How did all of these people know that I would arrive today? How do they always know!"

"Please, Miss Lind—"

"I came to New Orleans to sing, not to be trampled by a mob. Until it disperses, I refuse to leave the ship."

"If you will remain quiet for ten minutes," Mr. Barnum went on, "there will be no crowd. Good! Here comes Le Grand."

Jenny had only a glimpse of Le Grand Smith forcing a passage through the mass of people before she flounced off to her cabin. She found Josephine locking their trunks.

"No need to lock them," Jenny snapped. "We are not getting off."

Josephine, who had had a terrifying glimpse of the wharf through the window, said nothing as she took Jenny's cloak. Jenny's thoughts were still seething as she sat down on the edge of a chair. Le Grand Smith must have published the time of her arrival in the newspapers. That would be Mr. Barnum's idea of advertising her concerts! His methods were becoming intolerable.

Le Grand stood in the doorway. One sleeve was torn, but he was his usual urbane and charming self.

"Would you and Miss Ahmansson like to go up on deck now?" he asked. "If you lower your veil, no one will recognize you."

The twinkle in his brown eyes reassured Jenny. She took his arm. They reached the deck in time to see Caroline, a heavy green veil covering her face, join her father at the head of the gangplank. He tried to persuade her to descend —or so it seemed to the multitude waiting below.

"There's Barnum!" someone shouted from the wharf. "That must be Jenny with him."

The veiled figure appeared to draw back in alarm. After more earnest conversation, she was induced to walk down the gangplank. Le Grand stepped over to the railing.

"Open the way, please, for Mr. Barnum and Miss Lind," he called.

"Don't crowd her, gentlemen," Mr. Barnum exclaimed.

Pushing, coaxing, repeating his plea, he elbowed his way toward a waiting hack. As it rolled off down the street, hundreds in the crowd followed. They slowed the progress of the horses, but at least Caroline and her father were safe inside.

"Poor Caroline!" said Jenny. "I was so afraid she would be crushed."

"She probably enjoyed impersonating the Swedish Nightingale," said Le Grand drily. "Remember the time she sang with the choir in Baltimore?"

It was amazing how quickly the crowd on the wharf melted away. Within a few minutes Le Grand was able to escort the prima donna and her companion down the gangplank without attracting the slightest notice. He hailed another hack.

A three-minute ride brought them to the Place d'Armes, which recently had been renamed Jackson Square. The driver drew up before one of the handsome brick apartments known as Pontalba Row. The crowd had gathered here, and they stood looking up at a balcony calling for Jenny Lind. Amused by the situation, she crept up the stairs to the sumptuously furnished rooms which Le Grand had rented for her use.

Inside she found Mr. Barnum and Caroline. From below the windows came the insistent chant: "We want Jenny! We want Jenny!"

"Your admirers have been waiting for you, Miss Lind," said Mr. Barnum. "If you will wave to them, I am sure they will go away quietly."

She stepped out on the gallery and a moment later was smiling down into hundreds of new faces. At once she sensed the unique flavor of the city. Her first impression had been right. New Orleans was not quite of the New World, yet not quite of the old one either.

Two sides of Jackson Square were occupied by handsome red brick buildings. The wide galleries which ran the length of the second and third floors were enclosed by wrought-iron railings as delicate as lace in their design. Across the square she could see St. Louis Cathedral with its twin towers.

The cheers from the people who had come to welcome her were so spontaneous that Jenny forgot her recent bad temper. She leaned far over the railing and waved her handkerchief.

Whatever the charms of New Orleans, climate was not among them. For five weeks it rained nearly every day, and for that reason, perhaps, the people looked forward with even more than the usual enthusiasm to Jenny's concerts. Many also attended the lectures P.T. Barnum gave in the concert hall, when it was not needed for rehearsals. A teetotaler himself, he frequently made talks on temperance, and since there seemed to be more than the usual amount of drinking in New Orleans, he decided that some advice on the subject was in order.

Whatever the weather, Mr. Barnum managed to be his usual hearty self, but that was not true of his company. Several members were ill, and Jules Benedict fainted one morning at rehearsal. As orchestra conductor, accompanist, and piano soloist, he was onstage constantly during a performance, and he was feeling the strain.

In spite of the drizzly weather, the city wore an air of festivity. The concerts had been well advertised throughout the surrounding countryside, and a population of slightly more than a hundred thousand had been increased by ten thousand visitors. Many a planter who lived up the river had set aside a bale of cotton which he called "the Lind fund." This he sold and used the money to bring his family to New Orleans. Every boarding house was filled to over-flowing; tickets for every concert were sold out.

At the end of the fifth concert, Jenny decided that she had never sung before a more discriminating audience. She was elated by their eager response. All that seemed to matter at the moment was that she could sing and that people wished to hear her.

The next morning she was convinced that no career was worth the price she had to pay. She arrived at the theater a half hour before rehearsal to go over her correspondence with her secretary.

The first person she met was Giovanni Belletti, who passed her with only a coldly polite greeting. She saw the resentment in his face. Disturbed and puzzled, Jenny went on to the dressing room.

There, on a table, was a copy of a New Orleans newspaper which Max had laid out for her to read. One column had been marked—a review of last night's concert. As Jenny picked it up, her eyes fell on the words:

> *A grand overture was played by some forty or fifty musicians, of whom the celebrated Benedict was the leader. Then Belletti came forward and sang most beautifully. The tones of his deep, melodious voice fell most pleasantly on the ear.*

That was high praise. Giovanni should have been pleased. Jenny hastily scanned several paragraphs about her own numbers.

> *I don't care one farthing*—the reviewer said—*whether she sang correctly or incorrectly, scientifically or un-*

scientifically, whether she turned the notes right or turned them wrong. I know that after her first song, everything else seemed insipid; that Belletti's singing appeared very ordinary. . . .

Poor Giovanni! Jenny wished there were some way to ease his hurt pride. At the same time she was angry that he should blame her. As though she could give less than her best performance! she thought indignantly.

She was about to lay the newspaper down, when another story caught her eye. A few days before Mr. Kyle, the flutist in the orchestra, had brought a young man, scarcely more than a boy, to see her. The boy was a flutist, too, and he was blind. Friends in the village where he lived, some miles up the river, had taken up a subscription so he might come to New Orleans. An even greater thrill for him than attendance at Miss Lind's concert was the visit to her suite where she had sung a special song just for him. Other hotel guests with rooms on the same corridor must have heard her, but they could not possibly have known about the small sum of money she gave the boy to help with his musical education. It always irritated Jenny to have such gifts mentioned.

Who could have told the newspaper reporter? Mr. Barnum? Le Grand Smith?

At that moment, Max Hjortzberg came in with the mail.

"There are no letters that I cannot answer for you, Fröken Lind," he said, "but there is another matter I wish to call to your attention."

Jenny was still thinking about the story in the newspaper. She only half heard when Max reminded her that her sixty-first concert was scheduled for St. Louis the following week. One clause in her contract provided that she could cancel it at the end of the sixtieth performance.

"Yes, by paying a large forfeit," said Jenny.

"A compromise might be arranged," Max suggested. "Mr. Barnum has been cheating you outrageously—"

"With that I cannot agree," Jenny replied with spirit. "He has been liberal and fair."

"He can afford to be," said Max significantly. "He is coining money out of your genius. If I were your manager —"

"Please, Max!" Jenny sank down before her dressing table and removed her bonnet. "I cannot talk about it now —certainly not before rehearsal."

After the door had closed behind him, some of his words came back, staccato clear. She always defended Mr. Barnum to Max, but a seed of doubt had been growing in her mind. Only yesterday she had received a letter from John Jay, her lawyer in New York. He, too, had suggested that P.T. Barnum was exploiting her. It was true that Miss Lind was earning large sums, he said, but her manager had what the Americans called "the best of the bargain."

Jenny ran a weary hand over her forehead. She gladly gave her services when she sang for charity, but to sell them too cheaply was another matter. If only someone she trusted could advise her! Benedict was not well and certainly she could not talk to Giovanni in his present mood. She felt another thrust of indignation at the memory of his childish behavior. Hearing a knock at the door, she flung it open.

"So it's you, Mr. Smith," she said icily.

Le Grand ignored the storm signals in Jenny's face as he outlined the plans for the forthcoming voyage up the Mississippi River. Mr. Barnum had booked passage for the entire company on the steamboat *Magnolia*. The captain had agreed to stop over at Natchez and Memphis, long enough for a concert to be given in each town. Then Jenny would go on to St. Louis.

"We leave New Orleans this coming Saturday, on March 8, do we not?" she asked.

Le Grand cleared his throat. "That was the original plan, but Mr. Barnum has received a message over the new magnetic telegraph. The captain sends word that the *Magnolia* will be late arriving in New Orleans. We cannot leave here until Sunday noon."

Jenny looked at him in consternation. Le Grand, not understanding the reason, hastened to explain. "We shall reach Natchez and Memphis in time to give our concerts there."

"But, Mr. Smith, I cannot start a journey on the Sabbath. We must wait until Monday."

"That would be too late," Le Grand pointed out.

"Then the concerts will have to be postponed."

"They have already been advertised, Miss Lind. Tickets have been sold."

"No matter," said Jenny firmly. "It is against my principles to start a journey on the Sabbath."

The line of her jaw, the glint in her eyes, convinced Le Grand that it would be useless to argue. This was the first time he had been treated to a display of the Lind temper. To him it seemed inconsistent that her conscience should forbid her traveling on the Sabbath but condone her failure to keep two engagements on time.

When he reported the matter to Mr. Barnum his employer listened patiently. Not a line of disapproval deepened on his face.

"The *Magnolia* will have to delay its departure until Monday, as Miss Lind suggests," he said calmly. "Send a telegram to Natchez, postponing the concert there from Wednesday until Thursday evening. We'll give the concert in Memphis Friday morning—say, at eleven o'clock. Funny time for a concert, I know, but we can't wait until evening. Won't make connections with the St. Louis boat if we do."

Le Grand took out his handkerchief and mopped his face.

"I've heard you call Miss Lind an angel, and she is one on occasion. But again, like today, well, all I can say, Mr. Barnum, is that you have managed wonderfully in always keeping her angel side outside with the public."

"She's human like the rest of us," said Barnum mildly, "and like most persons of uncommon talent, she has a strong will."

"She certainly has!"

"But if she loses her temper, she regrets it and tells you so. And something else," Barnum added with a sly wink. "You might let the newspapers know about Jenny's refusal to travel on the Sabbath. Lots of folks feel the same way."

How like Barnum to turn a disadvantage into good advertising, thought Le Grand.

"All right," he said good naturedly. "I'll go out and send those telegrams."

When he crossed Jackson Square, he found it crowded. In the distance he could hear a brass band, the music gradually growing louder. Down Chartres Street came a parade of the New Orleans Association of Firemen, an organization which had shared in the funds raised at one of the benefit concerts. A door opened off the second-floor gallery of Pontalba Row. Jenny and Josephine came out, followed by Benedict and Belletti. The crowd in the square began to cheer. Jenny drew slightly closer to Giovanni, as though she wished to share with him the honors meant for her. Le Grand was puzzled. Belletti made no secret of his feelings, but what Jenny felt toward him no one could guess. Perhaps not even Jenny Lind herself.

As each company of firemen marched past, the men doffed their hats. Jenny curtsied and waved her handkerchief, seeming to take a childlike pleasure in the scene. When the Firemen's Band paused and began to play

"Home, Sweet Home," she leaned over the railing, a half smile parting her lips. She watched as one member of the Band fastened a mammoth bouquet to the end of a long pole and handed it up to her. This was the first time she had ever been presented with an offering of flowers in such a novel and unconventional manner. When she laughed, the hundreds of her admirers who had gathered in Jackson Square to watch, laughed with her.

Le Grand Smith, standing among the others in the crowd, shared with them a sudden surge of affection. Each person there felt that Jenny Lind's smile was meant for him. With a wave of her hand, unassuming, almost timid, she drew them all within the circle of her friendship. Another contradiction, Le Grand thought. A woman who hated crowds but loved people.

"God bless her!" he heard someone murmur.

It was the same reaction he had noticed at the concerts, but Jenny did not even need to sing. Mr. Barnum's "angel," he decided, as he hurried off to send his telegrams, could be forgiven a few inconsistencies.

13 §§

A Surprising Proposition

To Jenny Lind her decision not to start a journey on the Sabbath was not inconsistent. It was a matter of principle, and many of her contemporaries shared her point of view. She had once refused to give a command performance before the king of Sweden on a Sunday, and she saw no reason why she should forsake her convictions because a steamboat captain happened to be late. What she did regret was her angry outburt against Le Grand.

She felt actually ill with worry and fatigue by the time she boarded the *Magnolia* on Monday morning, and she did not leave her cabin for two days. On Wednesday, when she joined the rest of the party at breakfast, she still looked tired. Le Grand pulled out a chair for her and sat down beside her.

She spoke in a low voice, apologizing for her impatience a few days before. Her regret was so genuine that Le Grand wondered why he should have felt so irritated.

Later, walking the deck with him, she was fascinated by the rapidly changing aspects of the Mississippi. It was an unpredictable river, placid one moment, rising in great waves the next. Jenny was surprised by the amount of traffic. A number of steamboats roared past, with a shrill clanging of bells, on their way down to New Orleans. Still others chugged upstream, their giant paddlewheels churning the yellow water into foam.

"The finer vessels are called floating palaces," Le Grand explained.

He offered Jenny his arm as they descended the broad stairway to the ladies' salon, where she was to sing for the other passengers. She glanced at the tall mirrors which reflected a room with gleaming chandeliers, comfortable chairs, and wide divans upholstered in rich fabrics. The *Atlantic* had been no more impressive.

"The other floating palaces?" she asked. "Are they all as luxurious as the *Magnolia?*"

"Indeed, no, Miss Lind. For this voyage, for *you*, Mr. Barnum chose the finest steamboat on the river."

Others evidently wanted to travel on a luxurious boat, because it gave them a chance to spend some of their recently acquired riches. Jenny had heard of the gold rush to California, and many of the adventurers who had gone there hoping to make a fortune almost overnight had actually succeeded. Some of the passengers on the *Magnolia* were just back from California, their boots still caked with mud, carrying bags weighted down with gold nuggets. To one member of Jenny's troupe, who stood watching several of the men play cards, they seemed bent on gambling away the wealth they had gained so quickly. They were so intent on their game that only one of them even seemed aware that a concert had begun.

This man turned his head to listen. "Is that Jenny Lind singing? I'd give five dollars any time to hear her."

"It won't cost you any five dollars," one of the other players reminded him. "Just lay down your cards and mosey over to the ladies' salon."

"Not on your life. Not with this hand I'm holding now. Still, I always have had a hankering for music."

The next hour was doubtless a time of trial for the music-loving gambler. The rich sweet notes of Jenny's voice could be heard faintly in the distance, and every now and then he looked longingly in the direction of the ladies' salon. Once he pushed back his chair and started to get up. Then he sat down again, his gaze riveted on the cards in his hand. Even if he won the game, he had lost his chance to hear the Swedish Nightingale.

As it turned out, Jenny was more appreciative of the gamblers' musical abilities than they were of hers. That evening she heard them singing "Oh! Susannah:"

> *"I soon shall be in Frisco,*
> *And then I'll look around;*
> *And when I see the gold lumps there,*
> *I'll pick them off the ground.*
> *O California,*
> *That's the land for me*
> *I'm bound for San Francisco*
> *With a washbowl on my knee."*

This song by a young Pittsburgh composer, Stephen Foster, had been sweeping the country. It was a favorite with the gold-seekers who had been crossing the country on horseback, in covered wagons, and even on foot, in ever-increasing numbers. Jenny liked the songs with their lilting tunes and authentic American flavor, and Mr. Barnum agreed it would be a good idea to add some of them to her repertoire.

Late Thursday afternoon, the *Magnolia* tied up at the landing place at the foot of the hill where stood the little town of Natchez, Mississippi. March here was like summer farther north, and the heat was stifling. The small chapel in which the concert was held was jammed to the doors, and Jules Benedict was obliged to conduct his orchestra from the minister's reading stand. Jenny stood on the tiny makeshift stage, gazing at her audience in her simple unaffected manner. As always, when she sang, her face seemed transfigured. The murmur that greeted the end of each number was even more heartwarming than the thunder of applause which followed.

After the concert, the musicians descended to the landing place to find that the *Magnolia* had mysteriously disappeared. The members of the orchestra were alarmed. Had the boat pulled loose from the cables by which it had been attached to the wharf? Would they be forced to spend the night in this village? Only Jenny seemed to enjoy the delay. She was in a teasing mood and poked fun at their fears.

Benedict and Belletti were reassured. It was evident that Jenny had information concerning the curious ways of American steamboats which the others did not possess.

"What a night!" said Benedict, mopping his brow. "What a place to give a concert! There was hardly room to lift my baton. My men were not at their best, but *you*, Miss Lind! I never heard you in better voice."

"Thank you," said Jenny absently.

She was standing between her two friends, lifting her face to the breeze that blew in off the river. The moon had risen, and sky and water were drenched in silver light. It was hard to realize that this was the same yellow stream on which they would soon resume their journey. The older musician looked at her curiously.

"The audience was small," he went on. "Few of them had much knowledge of music, I dare say. Why did you not spare yourself?"

Jenny seemed astonished that he should ask such a question.

"Why, Mr. Benedict," she replied, "I value my music too highly not to give it my best always."

Jules Benedict had his answer. Not only to the question he had asked Jenny, but to another unspoken question:

What was her appeal for large numbers of people who ordinarily would never attend a concert? Technique and talent alone could not explain it. No, it was because Jenny Lind made a conscience of her music. Her fundamental honesty enabled her to share her own love and reverence for her art with her listeners.

"Look, Mr. Benedict!" Jenny broke in on his thoughts.

Rounding a bend in the stream came the *Magnolia*. The captain had taken it to a place about a mile above the town for the purpose of "wooding up." Enough wood had been taken on board to stoke the furnaces for the next lap of the voyage.

The following morning, the sixtieth concert was given in Memphis. Within half an hour after the final number, the *Magnolia* was on its way again, sweeping up the river at fifteen miles an hour. A magnificent sight awaited those on board that afternoon, when they reached the southern tip of the state of Illinois. Here the Mississippi and the Ohio Rivers came together in a mighty churning of waters. Two other states could be seen from the deck, Kentucky on the right, Missouri on the left, their wooded banks like thick green walls reaching to the water's edge. Soon the *Magnolia* was on its way up the Ohio, and a short time later the Barnum party transferred to another vessel, the *Lexington*. It was crowded and uncomfortable, and everyone breathed a sigh of relief on reaching St. Louis.

When Jenny walked down the gangplank and stepped into a carriage, she looked out on a brown muddy world. Though St. Louis was a fast-growing city, it still had some of the characteristics of a frontier town. The horses floundered through mud in a pouring rain, but in spite of the weather the wooden sidewalks were crowded. Some of the onlookers were fashionably dressed. Others, who waved as the carriage passed, were men wearing buckskins and women in calico dresses and flapping sunbonnets. Between seven and eight hundred strangers had arrived from out-lying villages and farms to attend the concerts.

The party was no sooner settled in their rooms at the City Hotel than Mr. Barnum was surprised to receive a visit from Max. The young man hesitated just inside the door.

"Come and sit down, Mr. Hjortzberg," said Barnum. "What's on your mind?"

Max advanced into the room but remained standing.

"Miss Lind's concert tonight will be her sixty-first under your management," he said.

"Yes?"

"Sixty concerts have already been given," Max continued. "Miss Lind wishes to avail herself of one of the conditions of her contract and cancel the engagement."

Barnum was startled. For Jenny to cancel at this time would be a costly proposition for her. He had paid her $137,000 to date. According to the terms of her second contract, she would be obliged to repay him the difference between this sum and the thousand dollars per concert which their first agreement had specified. She would owe him $77,000.

"Did Miss Lind authorize you to give me this notice?" he asked warily.

Max nodded.

Something was wrong, Barnum decided. It was possible that Jenny had been given some bad advice, and he must proceed carefully. For a long time he had realized that Max wanted to be her manager.

"If you will come back in an hour," he spoke in a tone that gave no hint he was worried, "I shall give you my answer."

During that hour, the perplexed manager called on a friend, a St. Louis attorney named Sol Smith. They went over the contract together, and Barnum returned to his hotel. He seldom gave way to anger, but he was angry now.

It had taken courage to bring Jenny Lind to America, and under his management she had earned more money in a few months than during several years in Europe. The more he thought of it, the more he wondered if she knew of her secretary's strange proposition. When Max knocked on the door, Barnum was waiting.

"I am ready to settle with Miss Lind," he spoke in a matter-of-fact voice, "and to close the engagement at once."

Max paled. He evidently had expected an argument. Perhaps he would be asked to use his influence with Miss Lind. It certainly would be to the advantage of the secretary, if he could "persuade" her to reconsider.

"You already have advertised concerts in Louisville and Cincinnati," he protested.

"That's all right," said Barnum cheerfully. "You can take my contracts for printing and concert halls off my hands. I'll let you have them at cost. Mr. Smith and I will be glad to help you, if you wish, to get a start on your own hook."

For a moment Max was only a brash young man whose collar seemed too tight.

"That is—well, ah—very liberal of you," he said grudgingly.

An uncomfortable silence fell between them—at least, uncomfortable for Mr. Hjortzberg. He braced himself. Although the conversation had taken an unexpected turn, perhaps only one more bold suggestion was needed.

"We might be able to work out a compromise," he went on. "Suppose Miss Lind should wish to give fifty more concerts in this country. What would you charge to manage each concert?"

"A million dollars. Not a cent less." Barnum's mild blue eyes flashed fire. "Now we might as well understand each other. I do not believe Miss Lind authorized you to cancel her contract. If she has, bring me a letter from her."

Max bit his lip but he tried to brazen it out.

"That will not be necessary. I am acting as her agent."

Mr. Barnum ignored the interruption.

"When I see Miss Lind's request over her signature and when I have her check for $77,000, the amount she would owe me, I shall be ready to close our business connections at once."

"But why?" Max insisted. "Why not make a new arrangement? Miss Lind would pay you liberally, say a thousand dollars a concert."

"Because I hired Miss Lind and not she me, and I do not intend to take a penny less for my risk and trouble than the contract gives me. If you do not bring me her decision, I shall go to her myself."

The next morning Barnum cornered Max in the hotel dining room. Again he asked for the letter from Miss Lind. Max twisted uncomfortably in his chair.

"Can't you see it was a joke?" he said. "I only wanted to see what you would say to such a proposition."

"Was Miss Lind in on the 'joke'?" asked Barnum relentlessly.

Max took refuge in his native Swedish. Barnum turned and left the room.

The usual broad smile was lacking as he climbed the stairs to Jenny's parlor. He had known from the start that she might decide to leave his management after a hundred concerts. But for her to want to cancel now and not tell him herself was hard to understand. They had had their difficulties, but Jenny was always straightforward, even to the point of bluntness. He did not really believe that she knew about her secretary's strange proposition, yet there was a nagging doubt at the back of his mind. He had to know.

When she called "Come in," in answer to his knock, he found her having breakfast with Benedict and Belletti. All three were laughing.

"Mr. Barnum, have you heard the joke?" asked Jenny.

"Joke?" Barnum's heart sank. "It was true then?"

"Of course it is true," said Jenny merrily. "Benedict won. He came in first."

Barnum was bewildered.

"In the horse race," Jenny explained. "In the trotting match on the Prairie Horse Course here. Oh, hadn't you heard? None of us knew anything about it either, until we saw it in the newspaper. One horse was named Barnum, another was called Belletti. A third horse was named for me, but poor 'Jenny Lind' only came in third. The fourth horse, named for Mr. Benedict, was the winner."

Barnum's hearty laugh rang out. It was a shade too hearty. Jenny looked at him sharply.

"Is there anything wrong?"

"No, Jenny."

He seldom called her anything except "Miss Lind," but she seemed pleased.

"At least, not now, and there is nothing for you to worry about. You should be free of all worry, free as a bird, and I intend to keep it that way."

And so Jenny hadn't known! He was thankful for that. Well, she would never find out from him.

14

April and Mr. Barnum

Mr. Barnum's usual good spirits were fully restored by the time the company left St. Louis. Spring waited for them in Nashville. The day after their arrival he drove out into the country with Jenny and Caroline to visit The Hermitage, the stately, white-columned house which had been the home of President Andrew Jackson.

It was a perfect day for a drive. The trees were putting forth their first green leaves, forming a delicate veil against the sky. Redbuds bloomed by the roadside. On the way back to Nashville, Jenny suddenly held up a warning hand.

"Listen!" she whispered. "Is that a mockingbird? Please, Mr. Barnum, ask the driver to stop."

The driver pulled his horse to a halt and Jenny leaned forward, her eyes searching. Then she saw it, perched on a branch, a little bunch of gray feathers with white patches on wings and tail.

"There it is," she said softly. "This is the first one I have ever seen, except in a cage."

She sat quite still, as the mockingbird poured forth its varied song. When the carriage drove on, Jenny turned to Mr. Barnum.

"To think," she said, measuring the size of the bird with her hand, "that such a small thing should have so much power! I never cease to wonder at a singing bird."

The next morning the manager and his star met in the parlor of the Veranda Hotel to discuss the itinerary for the weeks ahead. A calendar lay on the table before them.

"The first of April!" she exclaimed. "It is seven months since I arrived in New York."

"Bless my eyes, so it is," Barnum replied. "Your concert here will be your sixty-fifth. After we leave Nashville, we go to Louisville and from there we take another steamboat for Cincinnati."

Belletti was standing in the doorway. "Do you wish to speak with me, Mr. Barnum?"

"Why, no." Barnum shook his head.

Belletti apologized for intruding. The door had no sooner closed behind him when it opened again. Joseph Burke, the concert master, appeared.

"I hope I'm not late," he said breathlessly. "I came as soon as I heard."

"Heard what?" asked Barnum.

"That we are changing the program for our concert to-morrow and that I am to play not one but two violin solos."

"Who told you that? Le Grand Smith?"

Burke nodded.

Barnum laughed. "That donkey! I'm on to him. No, Mr. Burke, we are giving exactly the same program that was planned."

Barnum turned to Jenny and continued their conversation. He had chartered the steamboat *Messenger* to take the party from Cincinnati to Pittsburgh. From there they would return to Baltimore and Philadelphia, thence back to New York.

This information had to be given piecemeal. Several times there were interruptions by members of the company who had been informed that their employer wanted to see them. Jenny was annoyed, Mr. Barnum amused.

"That Le Grand. That donkey!" he repeated. "Thinks he can bamboozle me, does he?"

Again the door was flung open. One of the musicians, a violoncellist, entered, looking wildeyed.

"Give it to me," he cried.

"Give you what?" Barnum was shocked into being serious.

"My telegram. Mr. Smith said you had it." Turning to Jenny he explained with frantic haste. "My wife is expecting a baby. She said she would send me a message over the magnetic telegraph."

"So far as I know, no telegram has arrived," Barnum assured him, "but cheer up. Maybe you'll get one this afternoon."

P. T. Barnum, it seemed, was a good prophet. Later when Jenny met the violoncellist in the hall he was almost inarticulate in his excitement.

"I've had a telegram. My wife"—he gulped—"my wife has given birth to twins. I—I hadn't counted on twins."

"I am so glad for you," she said. "May I give a present to the twins? It would make me very happy."

The dazed father looked at her. He managed to say, "Thank you," before he rushed off to send a telegram to his wife. He was taking the first stagecoach for home.

To Jenny's bewilderment, several members of her company confided in her as the hours passed that they also had received telegrams. Burke, among others, had been asked to join an orchestra in New York. Max was offered a position in a bank. Benedict was urged to proceed at once to conduct an orchestra at the World's Fair then being held in London. Finally Belletti knocked on her door.

"Have you had an offer, too?" she asked.

He seemed surprised that she should know.

"Yes, to sing in London, at a better salary than I have

ever earned. A reporter from the Nashville *American* was here. I told him I thought I might take it. I was trying to compose an answer to my telegram, when I realized what it would mean—"

He looked at her apprehensively. "Jenny, I would not dare to leave you. What if I should lose you again?"

"That is a foolish way to talk!" She tried to keep the disappointment out of her voice. "If this new offer is to your advantage, you must accept it."

"I would not risk it—you in America, me in London! Unless we could be married now, *at once!* Why must we wait, *cara mia?*"

"At once? We do not know that we shall ever marry."

"That afternoon in Havana, you said—you promised—"

"I made no promise," Jenny found the old impatience rising within her. "Why, Giovanni, *why* must you always be so insistent? I thought that we agreed to wait. Certainly, the reasons for waiting have not changed."

Both were remembering that morning in New Orleans. Giovanni had fought his battle with himself; he had tried to conquer his jealousy. Nor had he realized that his anger had been so apparent.

When he spoke again, his tone was weary and resigned. "I shall not speak of this again, *cara mia*, before the end of the tour. You have my word."

A knock interrupted. Belletti opened the door to Le Grand Smith who held one of the telegrams.

"Miss Lind," he said, "I would like to talk to you. Do you mind?" He did not even seem to see Belletti, and Giovanni slipped from the room.

"Have you had bad news?" asked Jenny.

Le Grand handed her the telegram. It was signed by his father. The message stated that their village in Connecticut had been burned to the ground; the family homestead was in ashes.

"Le Grand! How terrible!"

The young man seated himself heavily in a chair. All the spark, the verve, had gone out of him.

"It is hard to believe that an entire village has gone up in flames. That my own home is gone—the house where my father and grandfather were born."

Jenny tried to comfort him, and to an extent she succeeded. At the end of an hour he rose and took her hand.

"Thank you for letting me unburden myself to you." He tried to look cheerful. "I'll be all right now, Miss Lind."

All that evening she was haunted by the memory of his stricken face. She slept fitfully and awoke almost as tired as when she had gone to bed. Josephine suggested a walk after breakfast. She felt sure that no one, certainly not Jenny, could remain depressed on such a bright spring morning.

Meanwhile Mr. Barnum had asked the other members of the company to assemble in the hotel parlor. They were waiting when he entered with a bundle of newspapers under his arm. The violoncellist tapped his foot impatiently; his carpetbag was packed, and his stagecoach would be leaving in a few minutes. Several of the other musicians seemed embarrassed. Because of the better offers they had received, they had asked to be released from their agreements with their present manager.

"The Nashville *American* is just off the press," he said innocently. "I have a copy for each of you."

By the time Jenny and Josephine returned, Mr. Barnum had made a discreet departure. Everyone else was hunched over a newspaper. Max Hjortzberg's cheeks were an angry red. Burke and Belletti looked chagrined, Benedict amused. The violoncellist clutched his forehead, disappointment shading into relief in the expression on his face. Le Grand Smith rose and made a place for Jenny beside him on the sofa. He handed her a newspaper.

"Oh!" her angry exclamation cut through the silence.

"A series of laughable jokes came off yesterday at the Veranda Hotel in honor of All Fools' Day," she read. *"We presume that many of the victims will first learn from our columns that they have been taken in by Mr. Barnum. He managed in some mysterious manner to obtain a lot of blank telegraphic despatches. Almost every person in the company received one. . . ."*

"April Fool's Day!" Burke gave a short laugh. "Guess we'll have to blame you, Le Grand. After what you put us up to, we might have known Barnum would get even."

"You mean that none of it was true?" Jenny gasped.

"No," Le Grand explained. "It was an April Fool joke. Barnum manufactured all those telegraphic messages himself."

"Your village, your home? They did not burn?"

Le Grand shook his head.

For a moment Jenny was too stunned to speak. "I am so glad," she said finally. "But what a cruel thing to do!"

"Oh, Barnum is a great practical joker. We don't mind a little horseplay, and we bear him no grudge," he assured her. "Besides, we'll find a way to get even."

This idea seemed to appeal to some of the other April Fool victims. There were exaggerated suggestions for revenge and considerable laughter. Jenny could find nothing amusing in the situation and swept from the room. She was halfway upstairs when Belletti caught up with her.

"There is another item in the newspaper," he said. "No one else has noticed it yet. Perhaps you will want to read it first."

She glanced at the paragraph he pointed out. It stated that Mademoiselle Lind was engaged to be married to her assistant artist, Giovanni Belletti.

"You must believe me, Jenny," he went on entreatingly. "I talked with that reporter, but I did not tell him that we were betrothed."

Jenny Lind with Giovanni Belletti and Jules Benedict by Sarony, New York, 1850.

Courtesy of The New York Historical Society, New York City.

Barnum's American Museum, c. 1851.
Courtesy of The New York Historical Society, New York City.

Iranistan, the home of P. T. Barnum.
Courtesy of the Barnum Museum, Bridgeport, Connecticut.

"What *did* you tell him?"

Belletti bit his lip. "The reporter said there was a persistent rumor that we planned to be married. He asked if I was in love with you, which I could not deny. I told him that I did not want to discuss it."

Jenny's glance sharpened. Had the reporter been given the wrong impression deliberately? Had Giovanni hoped, if the story was published, she would be forced to a decision? No, she felt sure he merely had been indiscreet in parrying some difficult questions, but unfortunately the result was the same.

"Then you and I need not discuss it," she said, and hurried upstairs to her room.

Even after more than twelve years in the public eye, Jenny was still distressed when untrue statements were printed about her. Her thoughts returned to Mr. Barnum. She felt more irritated each time she thought of his absurd little comedy.

The following morning the majority of the Barnum party left Nashville by steamboat. They were to sail up the Cumberland River, which emptied into the Ohio, then proceed up the Ohio to Louisville. There were no railroad connections between the two towns at that time, and several of the musicians decided to travel by stagecoach, which would give them an opportunity to visit Mammoth Cave. Jenny's curiosity about the cave was no greater than the curiosity about her on the part of some of the country people. When the driver of the stagecoach pulled the horses to a halt near a spring by the side of the road, she found an impromptu audience. Farmers in overalls and their wives wearing aprons over calico dresses were waiting in the hope that she would sing for them.

The request was made rather diffidently by one of the men, but Jenny did not hesitate. She stepped out into the dusty road and began her first song.

Though the famous prima donna had sung before many

brilliant audiences, no ovation had ever sounded sweeter, more sincere, than the applause that followed. Her good humor restored by the incident, she climbed back into the coach and leaned from the window to wave good-by. Mr. Barnum's unpleasant "joke" and her irritation with Signor Belletti seemed to be forgotten by the time the party reached Mammoth Cave.

None of them had ever seen anything like this great natural phenomenon. A guide carrying a torch led the way through a winding, twisting labyrinth between walls of rock and jagged stones. Jenny, walking just behind Joseph Burke, clung to his arm, not so much frightened as awed by the strange underground world. The guide flashed his torch, and they found themselves in a cavern that reminded them of a Gothic chapel. Farther on, he pointed out what he called the Bottomless Pit, so deep that no one had ever been able to determine how far it reached down into the earth.

Another hour's wandering brought them into a part of the cave so wide they could not see its boundaries. The guide flashed his torch toward the ceiling of the cave—or was it a sky? A somber sky, pierced, it seemed, with stars. Suddenly the guide withdrew with his torch, leaving the group in complete darkness. Jenny reached out for Joseph, but instead it was Giovanni who took her hand. There was something comforting and reassuring in his presence and she did not try to draw away.

Then, to everyone's astonishment, the deep rich tones of a violin broke the silence, and Jenny remembered that Joseph Burke had brought his instrument with him. He was playing the music of the "Prayer" from *Der Freischütz*, the opera in which she and Giovanni had often sung. The memory of that moment stayed with them long after they had emerged from the cave again into the sunlight.

Even the next morning when the journey was resumed, it

was hard for Jenny to realize that another exhausting round of rehearsals and concerts lay ahead. Ten miles out of Louisville, she was abruptly brought back to reality. Four white horses hitched to an elegant coach could be discerned in the distance, then coming closer and closer. The coach was occupied by a committee of prominent citizens who informed Jenny that they had come to escort her into the city. She was given the seat of honor in the coach and, in the words of the town's leading newspaper, she "entered Louisville in a blaze of glory."

The members of the company who had traveled by steamboat had already arrived, as had Señor Salvi. He was the Spanish tenor who had agreed to join the troupe as soon as the opera season in Havana was over, and Jenny was glad to welcome him. Señor Salvi was an excellent musician and added much to the success of her concerts that week, but as usual most of the applause was for Jenny Lind.

Though her reception in Louisville was noisy and enthusiastic, an even noisier welcome awaited her in Cincinnati. Jenny had her first view of this city from the deck of an Ohio River steamboat. Although it was only six in the morning, the wharf was black with people. She strained her eyes, hoping to see Le Grand Smith, who had arrived in advance of the rest of the party. There he was, pushing his way toward the gangplank. The instant it touched the ground, he was on it. The crowd surged forward, but police barred the way.

Jenny clenched and unclenched her hands. "What shall I do? I can never make my way through that crowd. This time I will not allow Caroline to do it either."

"It wouldn't do any good to try," said Le Grand ruefully. "The Buckeyes are on to you, Mr. Barnum. That story about New Orleans was in the papers here."

"Buckeyes?" asked Jenny, perplexed.

"A nickname for the people of the state of Ohio," Barnum explained. "So all those folks down there are expecting my daughter to walk down the gangplank, are they? That makes everything easy. If you'll pull down your veil, Miss Lind, and take my arm, we'll go ashore right now."

Somewhat hesitantly Jenny obeyed. She was halfway down when she heard Le Grand's voice from above.

"That's no go, Mr. Barnum. You can't pass your daughter off for Jenny Lind this time."

The crowd roared with laughter.

One man elbowed his way to the foot of the gangplank. "You may humbug the New Orleans folks," he shouted, "but you can't put it over the Buckeyes."

"Please, gentlemen, don't crowd her," said Barnum affably. "Will you allow us to pass?"

His grin was infectious and the crowd seemed to enjoy his little joke. They stood back, watching him help the veiled figure into a carriage. As the driver cracked his whip, Jenny stole a backward glance over her shoulder. All eyes were turned again toward the boat. Although the ruse bothered her, she could not help smiling.

Caroline and Josephine, peering through the window of their stateroom, saw the crowd gradually melt away. In less than an hour, Le Grand walked with them down the gangplank. As they stood waiting for a hack, they overheard some good-natured grumbling. Too late the curious onlookers were beginning to realize that they had been deceived by the fact that Barnum had *not* deceived them. The veiled figure on his arm had been the Swedish Nightingale, just as he said.

"Guess old Barnum was right," one man was heard to say. "He claims there's a sucker born every minute. Well, we certainly were suckers."

"He humbugged us after all," said another.

15 §§

A Touch of Melodrama

A country of strange contrasts, this America!

At the end of the voyage up the placid Ohio, between shores lightly touched by spring, Jenny and her party arrived in Pittsburgh. It was a foggy morning. The fog mixing with the smoke from hundreds of blast furnaces rose in dark dense clouds that obscured any view of the city. Even the people waiting on the wharf could be seen only dimly, as through a mist.

Jenny did not realize how large the crowd was, nor did Mr. Barnum, until they reached the foot of the gangplank. There the crowd closed in on her. Mr. Barnum's booming voice could be heard above the noise demanding that a path be cleared. It was a good ten minutes before they reached a carriage for the drive to Monongahela House.

Jenny, unaccustomed to the smoke, began to cough as she sank down on a sofa in the hotel parlor. Mr. Barnum brought her a glass of water.

"If there were any policemen on the wharf," he fumed, "I didn't see them. The police force in this city must be woefully inadequate."

Jenny clutched her throat and took a sip of water.

"Would you like to go to your rooms now, Miss Lind?" Barnum asked anxiously. "You have several hours to rest before the concert. You'll feel better by evening."

When Jenny arrived at the hall some time later, she was obliged to leave her carriage and make her way through another dense throng. A large part of her audience planned to hear her without paying. They stood in vacant lots, they sat on fences and leaned from windows of houses close by. A number of young rowdies pressed their faces against the windows of the hall itself. Their shouts and howls all but drowned the music of the overture. The orchestra could scarcely be heard.

Belletti fared no better. His songs were received with catcalls, and toward the end of each number one young blade imitated the crowing of a cock. Ushers hastily closed the windows, whereupon the crowd outside began muttering threats and insults. Jenny appeared on the stage, determined as always to give a good performance, but she could scarcely be heard.

"By hookey, is that all the louder she can sing? Call that singing? Can't even hear it!" The mutterings became roars. The roars swelled into a single word:

"Louder! Louder! Louder!"

"Sh! S-h-h-h-h!" A few feeble attempts inside the hall to restore quiet were almost as disturbing to a performer as the noise from without. Jenny, with a glance at Jules Benedict, waited for it to subside before she began her next song.

With each suceeding number the mob outside the building grew more demanding. If they could not hear, then no one else should! More catcalls added to the din, and the uneasy audience glanced at their programs. The next number was a selection from *Der Freischütz*. Jules Benedict lifted his baton. Jenny clasped her bouquet a little tighter and began:

> *"How every pulse is flying*
> *And my heart beats loud and fast. . . ."*

Her own heart was beating fast, and she was afraid it might stop altogether when she heard the sharp sound of breaking glass. One of the rowdies outside had tossed a stone through a window. No one was hurt, but several women screamed and Jenny was badly frightened. Her voice shook but she finished the song.

A burst of applause rewarded her, though only a few people in the front rows had been able to hear the music. Automatically Jenny made a curtsy, but all she wanted at that moment was to flee to the safety of her hotel room. To her dismay, when she and her co-artists started to leave the hall, a crowd was waiting in front of the main entrance. Barnum hastily closed the door and stepped back inside with the others for a hurried conference. In view of Jenny's popularity, he was puzzled by the attitude of the mob, but he was convinced that they meant her no harm.

"They only want to see you," he assured her, "but you won't have to face them. The rest of us will go on to the hotel. Perhaps we can distract the crowd. I dare say after a few minutes the stragglers out front will get tired and leave."

Jenny nodded. She was too terrified to speak. Two members of the business staff, Seyton and Bushnell, stayed with her. Seyton put out the lights, but the multitude outside could not be fooled so easily. They were prepared to wait all night, if necessary, for Jenny to appear. After a half hour she could bear the suspense no longer.

"Surely there must be some other way to leave this building," she spoke in a low voice.

"I'll find out," Mr. Seyton replied and was gone.

It seemed a long time, but actually it was only a few minutes before he returned. He held a candle, carefully shaded with one hand, and beckoned mysteriously. At the back of the hall there was a second entrance, protected by a high board fence. A five-dollar bill had accomplished wonders. Several boards had been pried loose to form an opening.

On the other side a strange vehicle waited. It was a dray ordinarily used for hauling freight. Seyton and Bushnell helped Jenny to climb inside, and the driver set off by a roundabout route through alleys and dark streets for Monongahela House. Mr. Barnum was waiting for them.

"Bless my eyes! I'm glad you're here, Miss Lind."

Never one to mind a touch of melodrama, he was inclined to make light of Jenny's unconventional ride. But when he saw how tired she was, his expression changed to one of deep concern.

"I regret what has happened more than I can ever tell you," he went on. "I am seeing the mayor of Pittsburgh tomorrow. I shall insist on police protection at our second concert."

"Our second concert?" Jenny flared. "Do you think you could induce me to sing here again? I intend to leave at the first possible moment."

Mr. Barnum did not answer at once. Finally he said, "There's a steamboat leaving early in the morning."

Nothing was said about the inconvenience caused by the abrupt change in plans. Mr. Barnum made no mention of the money he would lose, as he went on to outline the roundabout route to Baltimore where the next concerts were scheduled. The steamboat could take Jenny and her party only a short distance, and the journey across the Allegheny Mountains must be made by stagecoach. Mr. Bushnell was leaving Mr. Barnum's employ but would escort them as far as Cumberland, Maryland, where they would change to the railroad cars.

Several members of the company lingered in Pittsburgh to assist their manager. Mr. Barnum wrote letters to the newspapers and had placards posted in the business district, explaining as best he could why the second concert had been canceled. Money would be refunded to all who had bought tickets. He paid the rent for the hall and settled numerous business details.

The following afternoon he had reason to be grateful that Jenny and her co-artists were safely on their way across the mountains. A neatly dressed woman knocked at his door, and she brought disturbing news.

"Mr. Barnum," she told him, "I happened to overhear a conversation which I believe would interest you."

"What was that?" he asked, placing a chair for his visitor.

"You are going to Baltimore from here, is that not right?"

Barnum nodded.

"Then be careful. Some scoundrels are planning to stop your stagecoach as it crosses the Alleghenies and rob you."

"Why, that is incredible," Barnum protested. "This is not the Wild West any longer. This is 1851."

"I don't care what year it is," she retorted. "If you want to be robbed, it's no butter off my bread."

"Indeed, Madame, I appreciate your coming to warn me," said Barnum quickly. "But tell me how you came by this information."

The woman, somewhat mollified, explained that she had learned of the plot quite by accident. She had been passing along a lonely street, on her way to a friend's house, when she saw three rough-looking men approach. Not liking their appearance, she had stepped back into the shadow of a tree and waited for them to pass by.

Instead, they had chosen that spot to continue their conversation. She had heard every word, as they outlined their plan to rob the stagecoach. She dared not think of what might have happened to her if they had known that anyone was listening. Mr. Barnum tried to assure her that she was in no danger.

"But you are," she said anxiously. "The stagecoach travels a lonely route, and those men seemed to know that you carry large sums of money with you."

"They are in for a surprise," Barnum replied. "I shall take every precaution."

After his caller had left, he estimated how much money would be needed to pay expenses as far as Baltimore. The rest of his cash he took to a bank and arranged to have it remitted to New York. Although he did not like to alarm his companions, he believed it necessary to take them into his confidence. He bought several revolvers. When the stagecoach began its lonely journey across the mountains, every occupant was armed.

Armed and alert! Whenever the horses slowed for a climb up a steep trail, each man would grasp his pistol tighter. Every overhanging ledge of rock, every cluster of trees or a thick growth of bushes seemed to offer possibilities for an ambush. The coming of darkness increased the tension. Because thieves were more likely to strike at night, sentries were appointed. Each took a turn keeping watch while the others slept.

It was Mr. Barnum's turn as the first pale streaks of dawn showed in the sky. For the past hour a suspicion had been growing in his mind. As soon as his companions awoke, he admitted it. They grinned sheepishly and put their revolvers back into the holsters.

On Barnum's arrival in Baltimore, he went at once to Jenny's hotel. Benedict and Belletti were with her, as was Le Grand Smith. The four of them seemed nervous and distraught. Barnum did not notice at the time that he had interrupted a conversation.

"Well, Le Grand," he asked, "am I right in assuming that you have had your revenge for April Fool?"

Le Grand kept his eyes on the ceiling. "Are you referring to a warning by a certain lady I know?"

"By thunder, she took me in all right."

"I believe I have heard you say," Le Grand went on innocently, "that folks like to be humbugged and the world is full of suckers."

"And I was one of them." Mr. Barnum roared in appreciation of his own gullibility. "You should have seen us, sitting on the edge of our seats, our revolvers cocked, all the way across the mountains."

Jenny had heard Mr. Barnum referred to as a humbug, and she had heard him speak of suckers. Now for the first time she undertood the meaning of the words. She almost forgot how provoked she had been with her manager when she joined in the laughter.

She and the others needed that laugh. Almost at once they grew serious again.

"We have bad news, Mr. Barnum, and this time it is no April Fool," said Le Grand. "Mr. Benedict wants to be released from his contract. He feels he should return to England."

"Leave the company?" asked Barnum in consternation. "Have you been ill again?"

Benedict shook his head. "No, but I am under great strain. There is hardly a moment during a concert when I am not on the stage. I conduct the orchestra. I have my own solos. I play Miss Lind's accompaniments."

"That is true," said Barnum regretfully. "We have expected you to do the work of two, possibly three musicians."

"When you came in," Jenny spoke for the first time, "we were talking about an accompanist for me." She seemed on the verge of making a suggestion, but her voice trailed off.

"It is not that I want to leave the company," Benedict went on. "This tour has been a remarkable experience and I regret going more than I can tell you."

"Perhaps it will not be necessary," Barnum suggested. "Would you consider staying on as conductor if you could be relieved of your other duties? Let's say we can find another pianist who can accompany Miss Lind to her satisfaction—"

"I know a young man who may be able to come," Jenny interrupted.

"Is he in New York?" asked Barnum.

"No, in Germany. He is only twenty-two, but an excellent musician. He accompanied me in several concerts in Germany and England."

"His name, Miss Lind?"

"Otto Goldschmidt."

She was aware of the silence. Mr. Barnum had never heard of Otto Goldschmidt. There was silence from Belletti, too. She looked at Benedict appealingly.

"I know young Goldschmidt," he said. "We should have thought of him before. You could not do better, Mr. Barnum."

"Then you would stay on as conductor?"

Bendict seemed to consider. He was homesick for his family, but at the same time he disliked the thought of leaving. Moreover, he had signed a contract, and he owed a certain loyalty to Jenny.

"Yes," he said slowly. "I would like to stay, under those conditions."

"Then as far as I am concerned, the matter is settled," said Barnum. "The only question is: Will this young what's-his-name be willing to come so far on such short notice?"

"I believe he might!" Jenny jumped up in a flurry of skirts.

Gone was the famous prima donna. She was looking up at her manager intently, relieved and pleased at the easy solution of their problem.

"Would you like me to write him, Mr. Barnum?"

"Yes, would you?" he asked. "We'll send the letter on the fastest steamer."

After the others had gone, he stayed for a few minutes to discuss financial terms. Jenny sat down at the desk, drew a sheet of notepaper toward her, dipped the quill pen into the ink.

"Dear Otto . . ." she began.

She was humming softly under her breath.

16 §§

Goodby, Mr. Barnum

The eighty-fifth concert! Jenny stood beside Signor Belletti in the wings of Tripler Hall in New York City listening to her new pianist. She nodded approvingly. Otto Goldschmidt lacked Benedict's stage presence, but his playing
showed remarkable maturity for such a young man.

From beyond the footlights came a subdued but, to the
keen ear of a performer, an ominous sound. People were
stirring restlessly in their seats. Otto struck the final chords.
Then silence.

"Why doesn't the audience applaud?" Jenny whispered
to Belletti. "Poor Otto!"

Belletti choked down his fury. Poor Otto, indeed! He
was only sharing the fate of all musicians who must appear
on the same program with Miss Lind.

At last came a faint spatter of applause. It must not be allowed to die down, Jenny resolved. Belletti watched in
amazement as she walked on the stage. Her gloved hands
made no sound as she applauded, but the audience took
their cue from her. Many were clapping now. Jenny shook
hands with Otto, congratulating him on a fine performance.
The applause became almost an ovation. In response Jenny
curtsied, not to the audience but to the pianist.

During his second solo, she seated herself on a chair near

the piano, and listened attentively to every note. At the end she stepped forward to shake hands again and to repeat her congratulations. The young man flushed with embarrassment—and pleasure.

Belletti who had forced himself to watch from the wings turned quickly away. Whenever he had complained of an indifferent reception, it was because he was jealous. Or so Jenny seemed to think. Yet she had practically forced an ovation out of the audience for this newcomer. It was all Signor Belletti could do to be polite to Mr. Goldschmidt the next time they met.

The meeting took place a few days later in Jenny's sitting room at Irving House, where they were joined by Benedict and Burke to witness a parade. Months had passed since Mr. Barnum had conceived the idea of presenting a traveling museum and menagerie. His partner in the enterprise had recently sailed home from Ceylon with a cargo of wild animals.

The music of a band called Jenny and her guests to the balcony. Up Broadway came the parade which was to introduce Mr. Barnum's latest enterprise to the American public. In the lead were ten giant elephants, richly caparisoned and pulling a mammoth Oriental chariot. Next came a cavalcade of more than a hundred high-stepping horses, followed by a three-months'-old elephant three and a half feet high.

"Oh!" Jenny leaned forward, a smile tugging at her lips.

In the howdah on the baby elephant's back rode General Tom Thumb, the famous midget Mr. Barnum had exhibited both in Europe and in America. He was a cocksure young fellow, who drew himself up to his full height of twenty-seven inches when he waved his small cocked hat.

There were prolonged cheers from the spectators who lined Broadway. Five minutes later they appeared to be just as interested in a cage full of lions. They laughed uproariously at several long-legged ostriches with their peculiar humping walk. Each new feature of the parade was greeted with the same indiscriminate enthusiasm.

Jenny turned back into her sitting room, tired and depressed. It was just such a crowd that had followed her carriage in New York when the novelty of her coming was still fresh. Did she mean no more to those people down in the street than one of Mr. Barnum's big lumbering elephants?

This stabbed deep, and hurt pride helped her to come to a decision she had been trying to make ever since that trying night in Pittsburgh. After her return to New York, she had talked with Mr. Jay, her lawyer, about the wisdom of bringing her tour to a close after the one hundredth concert. The clause in her contract which would make this possible also required her to pay a forfeit of twenty-five thousand dollars. That was a large sum, but she no longer hesitated.

"I'm going to cancel my contract," she announced with sudden resolution. "That means that we shall give—let me see—fifteen more concerts for Mr. Barnum."

Otto was looking at her in surprise, the others in consternation. Belletti was the first to speak.

"You mean give up the tour? Return to Europe?"

Jenny had not thought that far. Certainly her assistant artists must not be made to suffer by her decision. Benedict, partly through loyalty to her, had stayed on as conductor. Otto had made a long voyage at her suggestion. It would not be fair to them and the others of the company, to bring the tour to an abrupt close.

"We shall not return to Europe for several months, if you are willing to stay with me," she replied. "I would like to give a series of concerts under my own management. Mr. Seyton and Max can handle the business details."

Belletti could not hide his disappointment. He and Mr.

Barnum had become good friends, each man warming instinctively to the spontaneity of the other.

"You never had a better manager," he said.

"Perhaps, but he is a showman." Jenny's lips tightened. "He has exhibited me as he does his big giant or any of the other freaks in his museum. I refuse to be exhibited much longer."

Once her decision was made, she felt lighthearted and happy again. Never to have to sing before another "Barnumish" house! She could find no other way to describe the audiences whipped to a frenzy of enthusiasm by extravagant advertising. She would tell Mr. Barnum that evening.

The right words did not come so easily when he was sitting across from her. She liked this big hearty man as much as she disliked his methods. He had been considerate and fair, and she was sorry that she must disappoint him.

He did not seem as surprised at her decision as Jenny had expected. His bland smile suggested that he, too, was glad the tour was nearly over.

For Mr. Barnum was tired. A tour of four thousand miles was enough to tire any man, even a showman with a skin as tough, so many people thought, as one of his own elephants. Every day for more than eight months, he had been beset by anxieties, not the least of which was Jenny herself. Her admirers, intrigued not only by her voice but by her sweet and unassuming manner, had readily believed Mr. Barnum's publicity.

He believed it himself. Her natural impulses, as he said later, were "more simple, childlike and pure" than those of any person he had ever met. So what did it matter if fatigue and the constant straining for perfection that were part of her nature resulted in occasional outbursts of temper? Of these, few people ever knew. Mr. Barnum had taken every precaution that, to the public, Jenny Lind should remain an angel.

The angel's impresario heaved a sigh. It would be good to retire to Iranistan and *rest.*

"Will you continue to sing under another management?" he asked.

"My own," she replied promptly. "There are members in my own company who will be willing to act as my agents."

"I—see." Mr. Barnum feared that if Jenny gave concerts on her own account, she would be imposed on. But let her try it! In no other way would she be convinced that his own management had been in her best interests. Young Max had been itching to be her manager.

"I think perhaps Mr. Hjortzberg would be willing," said Barnum drily.

Max was elated when he heard the news. He repeated the familiar accusation: Barnum was nothing but a showman, a humbug. Miss Lind would do much better on her own— with her secretary's help, of course. His cool assumption of authority made her uneasy. She reminded him crisply that fifteen more concerts had been scheduled by Mr. Barnum.

Seven of these were in New York. The last eight were to be given in Philadelphia and Boston. Jenny arrived in Philadelphia the end of the first week in June. This was her third visit, and she was glad to be back.

A Sabbath hush had fallen over the Quaker City, when she and Josephine drove to church on Sunday. Jenny leaned back against the cushions. She took a deep breath, enjoying the fragrance of a June morning. The trees in Independence Square were in full leaf, and through an occasional gateway she had a glimpse of a garden. Most of the red brick houses she passed were of Georgian design and set flush with the street. Philadelphia still looked very much like an English town.

Yet, as Jenny knew, several years before William Penn's Quakers had laid out their City of Brotherly Love, a group of her own countrymen had established new homes only a few miles away. Others had followed, and traces of those early Swedish settlements still remained.

When the carriage rolled to a stop before the Old Swedes' Church, now mellow with age, the big square belfry and steep-gabled roof were vivid reminders of her homeland. Men and women of Swedish descent had been worshiping inside the ivy-covered walls for a century and a half.

All eyes were turned in her direction when she joined in singing "A Mighty Fortress Is Our God." On this morning she did not seem to mind the stares. She felt herself to be among her own people. At the end of the service Jenny stepped out into the June sunshine with a feeling of peace and tranquility that stayed with her all day.

This feeling was rudely shattered on Monday when Max drove with her to rehearsal. She learned for the first time that her concerts were not to be given at the Chestnut Street Theatre, where she had sung on her earlier visits. No, Max spoke with biting sarcasm, Mr. Barnum had selected the National Theatre, recently vacated by a circus.

"Why, Miss Lind"—he paused delicately—"it still reeks of the stable. It is incredible that you should be expected to sing in such a place."

Jenny made no reply as Max opened the door and followed her into the theater. The first person that she saw was her unsuspecting manager. She fairly flung the words at him:

"Mr. Barnum, please understand that I am not a horse."

The shooting sparks in Jenny's eyes warned Mr. Barnum that she was not joking. Max stood behind her, a smile twisting his thin lips.

"I have been informed," Jenny went on icily, "that a circus performed here recently. Not that I needed to be told. That fact is evident—"

She paused in confusion. She could detect none of the telltale odor of which Max had spoken. At that moment another young man who had been standing a few feet away turned toward her. It was Otto Goldschmidt. Jenny found herself blushing.

"Why, Miss Lind," Barnum replied, "the place has been thoroughly cleaned and fitted up for an Italian opera company which is to play here next. That was done even before I engaged the theater. It is in a very convenient location."

"I—I am sorry, Mr. Barnum. I spoke too hastily."

"That's all right," he assured her, but his face was troubled when he returned to his hotel.

Back in his room he sat down at his desk to decide what course he should take. More and more he and his star were getting on each other's nerves, and Max wasn't helping matters. Thus far Mr. Barnum and Jenny had remained on friendly terms. He hoped that they would still be friends when they parted.

"But with several concerts still to go—" He spoke aloud, leaving the sentence unfinished. He snapped his fingers. "I'll do it. I'll write to her at once.

He rummaged through the desk for a pen. In his letter he offered to release Jenny from her contract after that night's concert, if she so wished. In return, he asked that she pay an additional forfeit of a thousand dollars each for the seven concerts which she would not give. Barnum knew that he could earn several times that amount by holding her to her agreement. But what matter? He shrugged his big shoulders. The tour had proved profitable enough as it was.

Jenny had returned to her hotel when a messenger delivered the letter. She read it with a mixture of surprise, chagrin—and relief. Toward evening Barnum received her reply, written in her usual round firm handwriting.

"My Dear Sir: I accept your proposition to close our contract tonight, at the end of the ninety-third concert. . . ."

That evening Mr. Barnum visited Jenny backstage. Both

felt secretly thankful that their friendship was still intact. As she looked up into the big square face a rush of almost frightening responsibility swept over her. She had thought that she welcomed the challenge to give concerts on her own, but this was not Europe. This was America—Mr. Barnum's America. In this moment of parting, she knew how much she owed him. It was his kindness that she would remember.

Saying goodby was harder than either of them had expected.

three

Two Loves for a
Nightingale

17 §§

A Glimpse of Paradise

Jenny decided to give the concerts which Mr. Barnum had scheduled for Philadelphia and Boston. Because of the haste with which her new arrangements must be made, he permitted the use of the tickets already printed. Now if others would only be as considerate! The end of the partnership, coming so abruptly, was bound to cause talk and speculation.

The next morning, when Jenny arrived at the theater for rehearsal, she found Otto Goldschmidt backstage, absorbed in a newspaper. Although he still did not read English easily, there was no mistaking his distress.

"Why, Otto, what is wrong?"

It was too late to hide the newspaper.

"Nothing that would interest you, Fräulein," he said hastily.

Jenny held out her hand. "I wish to see it, please."

He handed it to her reluctantly. The editorial he had been reading predicted that Mr. Barnum's Nightingale was going to miss his wise counsel. "Indeed," the writer continued, "some of the journals are beginning to admit that Jenny Lind—'that angel,' 'that divinity'—is a woman, nothing more or less, a woman (with flesh, blood and temper). Some say she is a spoiled child. . . ."

She read no further. Of course she was a woman of flesh

and blood, yes, and temper, too. It was Mr. Barnum who had built up the myth of her perfection, and now she was being called a spoiled child. Her thoughts were seething as her glance fell on Otto. A more uncomfortable-looking young man she had never seen.

"Do not let it bother you," she tried to reassure him. "It is customary that a great deal of exaggerating is done at my expense."

She closed the door of her dressing room and stood leaning against it. She was touched by Otto's solicitude, reassured by his loyalty. All of her co-artists had been loyal, even though they may not have approved of her decision. Even Giovanni had spoken no word of reproach. With his help, with the help of the others, this independent tour under her own management would succeed. It must! Her pride demanded it.

As to how the tour should be managed, she had definite ideas. There should be no more auctions. Prices for tickets must be the same for all. As her chief agent, she chose Mr. Seyton. Max was disappointed to find himself only an assistant, but his temper was too uncertain to be trusted with the chief responsibility.

When the company arrived in Boston in the middle of June, a stack of mail was waiting at Revere House. Many of the letters were invitations for Jenny to sing, more than she could possibly accept. One letter came from Toronto, Canada, but Jenny shook her head. It was too far away, and Mr. Seyton left at once to arrange for some concerts in the western part of Massachusetts. Max reported an excellent sale for her five appearances in Boston's Tremont Temple.

Just being in Boston made Jenny's spirits rise. She hired a carriage and a pair of high-stepping horses, so that she might resume her custom of taking an afternoon drive. The first day Giovanni was her companion. The next day it was Otto. When the driver turned into Louisburg Square, she was filled with the same unaccountable delight she had felt the first time she saw it.

The tall elms in the little park were at their greenest and they cast long shadows on the tall mellow old brick houses.

"See that house, No. 20?" Jenny asked. "That is the home of my friends, Mr. and Mrs. Samuel Ward. I want you to meet them, Otto. I want you to meet the Honorable Edward Everett and Professor Longfellow, too."

"Thank you, Fräulein!" He was regarding her intently. "There is much to thank you for."

"I am proud to have you in my company," Jenny replied. "Whether you accompany me or I accompany myself, it is the same."

"I was thinking of my—my solos."

There was a painful pause. Since that night in New York, Jenny had made it a practice to sit on the stage while Otto was playing. He no longer lacked for applause, but it irked her that her presence should be necessary.

"Mr. Barnum used to say that the public is a very strange animal," she said. "A performer can never be quite sure how it will respond. You must not be discouraged. Remember, you are very young."

"Yes!" His voice dropped. "I'm not yet twenty-two."

They looked at each other across the gap of years.

"And I am thirty, closer to thirty-one. An *auld hag*, I would be called in Swedish."

The return drive to Revere House was made in almost complete silence. She opened the door of her luxurious suite to find Belletti in earnest conversation with Josephine. Josephine, in her usual self-effacing manner, vanished in the direction of the bedroom.

"Jenny!" Giovanni hardly waited until the door had closed before he began to speak. "Max is waiting to see you. He may be with you for hours. Can't we talk for a few minutes first—just you and I?"

He seemed to read her thoughts as she stood looking down at him.

"I know I am breaking my word," he admitted. "What else can I do, now that I find myself about to be supplanted?"

"Who is supplanting you?" asked Jenny evenly.

"Who else but Otto Goldschmidt? It used to be that I was your companion on your afternoon drives. Not only that!" he added quickly, giving her no chance to interrupt. "I am thinking of the way you sit on the stage during his solos. You force the audience to applaud! It never matters to you if I am received coldly."

Jenny's control snapped. "For shame, Giovanni! Otto is appearing with older and more experienced musicians. He has great talent. He needs our encouragement, and he deserves it."

"How like you, *cara mia!*"

Already Giovanni was ashamed of his outburst, as he sat down beside Jenny on the sofa.

"If I try your patience"—he reached out a hand and touched her cheek—"remember it is because I love you."

She could see the little wrinkles of pain at the corners of his eyes. Her impulse was to comfort him, but she restrained herself.

"Please say no more," she begged. "You know and I know: the wrong decision might mean lifelong unhappiness for both of us."

"I am unhappy anyway," he replied. "I do not expect perfection of marriage."

Yes, that was the difference between them, thought Jenny. She had always expected, she had always exacted, perfection. This trait had made her a great artist; it also had made her more intolerant. She could no more excuse shortcomings in others than in herself. She thought back to her two broken engagements—and was grateful. She remembered the stormy scenes between her parents when she was a child. Better no marriage at all than one without perfect love and understanding.

"You are right, Giovanni," she said quietly. "I do expect perfection."

The crowded days left her little time to brood over Belletti. After Boston, she and her five fellow artists moved on to Springfield. This was a considerably smaller company than had traveled with Mr. Barnum, and even the disgruntled Max finally admitted that the orchestra must be dispensed with if the tour was to show a profit.

Springfield proved to be a picturesque town rising on wooded terraces on the east bank of the Connecticut River. A private residence on Howard Street was turned over to Jenny and her friends for as long as they wished to stay. It was a comfortable house, gracious and with a touch of elegance, and Jenny wished that she could linger all summer.

The first afternoon she was awakened from a nap by the sound of voices, young voices calling her name. Josephine helped her slip into a dress, and she hurried out on the balcony. Her breath quickened as she looked down on more than a hundred boys and girls drawn up in marching procession in the street.

"There she is now! That's Jenny Lind! Hurrah for Jenny Lind!"

Jenny leaned over the balcony and waved. Another shout! She kissed her hand to the children. Never had she received an ovation that pleased her more.

That evening her business agents were invited for supper. Jenny glanced around the high-ceilinged room with family portraits on the walls.

"Why can't we make Springfield our headquarters?" she asked. "There are several railroad lines leading to surrounding towns. Could we not return here between concerts?"

She was looking at Mr. Seyton. "That would be a good

idea for a few days," he replied. "We have one concert scheduled for Northampton and one for Hartford in the adjoining state of Connecticut. You can go by special train to both towns and return here, if you wish. The other requests have come from cities in New York State."

He took a list from his pocket and read off the names: "Albany, Utica, Syracuse, Auburn, Rochester, Buffalo. . . . They are too far away to permit traveling back and forth. The trips would be too tiring."

"Very well," said Jenny wistfully, "but let us stay here as long as possible."

The Springfield concert took place in the old First Church in Court Square. The next morning a private carriage drawn by four white horses waited in front of the house on Howard Street. This was the day planned for a long drive, and this time Jenny invited both Giovanni and Otto to go with her. Seated in the carriage, her wide skirts spreading around her, she smiled impartially at the two men who sat facing her. The driver turned into a parklike area, in what was then the outskirts of the city. Here was the old arsenal, built during the American Revolution. The high tower had recently been added, and it was a steep climb of ninety steps to the top.

From that height Springfield looked a green blur, with only the church spires and the roofs of a few handsome houses emerging from the tangle of foliage. All around lay the lush valley cut through by the bright ribbon which was the Connecticut River. Farther away, to the south, rose the hills around Hartford. To the west Jenny could see the wooded foothills of the Berkshires. She stood looking at the view for a long time.

"I never saw anything so perfect," she said, as Belletti helped her back into the carriage. "Not even in Switzerland."

A long drive through the countryside brought the three

Europeans to the village of Northampton in time for tea.
Tall elms cast a benevolent shade on white houses sitting
primly behind white fences. The Old Church had its doors
flung wide as though inviting them to enter. Farther on,
from the top of a gentle slope, they saw a limpid pool, exquisite as a jewel in a setting of oaks and pines.

"Is that a lake?" Jenny asked.

"We call it a pond, ma'am," the driver replied. "The
children hereabouts call it Paradise Pond."

A perfect name! she thought, as they resumed their drive.
At the crest of Round Hill, the carriage stopped before a
big rambling hotel, and a few minutes later they were
seated at a table by the window. The neat white houses of
Northampton lay nestled in the lush valley below. To the
east, Mount Holyoke raised a green peak against the sky.

Jenny set down her teacup. She looked across the table at
her companions. "Do you feel as I do—"

It was hard to phrase her question. She herself could not
understand why she should be deeply stirred by this little
town. Suddenly she was aware that two pairs of dark eyes
were regarding her intently. Neither man was conscious of
the other. Jenny's heart sank.

Otto, too! she thought.

She did not want to see him hurt, but of course he could
not really be in love with her. There was too great a difference in their ages. One day he would make some fortunate
young Fräulein a wonderful husband. She wished that
Giovanni had some of the deep calm that underlay Otto's
youthful shyness.

Or did she? Belletti flashed her a smile, and she knew that
she would not have him other than he was. The traits which
irritated her, and which would make marriage to him a
succession of stormy scenes, were a part of his charm.

"Did you ask us a question, Fräulein?" Otto reminded
her.

Jenny was brought back to the present with a start. Otto, in his quiet way, had charm too. One had to hunt for it, but it was there.

"I was thinking that Paradise Pond is well named. But all of this—" Her glance took in the view of the tranquil village and the rolling countryside outside the window. "I'd call all of it Paradise. The Paradise of America. I am glad that we are coming back."

It was a very damp "paradise" to which they returned on Monday evening to give a concert. A sultry day had ended with a violent storm. The dark masses of cloud which had been piling up in the west let loose with torrents of rain and drenched the town. Yet the church was packed. Many in the audience had traveled long distances from villages and farms up and down the Connecticut Valley. Others came from as far away as the New Hampshire hills.

When Jenny stepped out on the wooden platform, which had been erected over the pulpit, the auditorium looked like a garden. Since it was the custom to throw flowers on a stage to honor a favorite performer, nearly everyone carried a bouquet. Outside the rain continued to fall in torrents and the storm increased in fury, but no one in the church seemed to notice. All eyes were on the tall girl in a white dress waiting to begin her first number.

Jenny could hardly be heard as she began the *"Casta Diva."* But the words of Norma's prayer seemed to restore her power, and her voice rose in triumph above the thunder.

"*. . . oh, bless us.*
Let thy peace shine on our night."

A blinding flash illumined the church with an almost unearthly brilliance, but the lightning was no brighter than the flash of revelation in Jenny's heart. In a single instant her doubts and indecision were swept away, and she realized with a start that the knowledge had lain buried deep in her thoughts for a long time. The audience saw the spreading radiance in her face.

During the rest of the program no one seemed conscious of the storm. After numerous encores the reluctant audience filed out into the rainy night. Never had she sung before such kindly people, thought Jenny, as she stepped into a side doorway leading from the church. She waited quietly, hugging her secret to her. When anyone passed, she drew back farther into the shadows. There was only one person she wanted to see. He had gone to fetch her cloak.

He was behind her, slipping the cloak around her shoulders. She leaned against him and felt him stiffen. She stiffened, too, and a flush mounted to her cheeks which she was glad no one could see. Age! Age! she thought ruefully. Whatever had come over her back there in the church? It was a relief to hear the crunch of wheels rolling down the street.

"The carriage is coming, Fräulein," said Otto in his usual respectful tone, "but hadn't we better wait until it stops raining?"

"Of course not," Jenny replied. "A special train is waiting to take us back to Springfield."

What did a little rain matter? She could be grateful that it had restored her common sense.

All Otto heard was the sharp tone of her voice.

18 §§

Jenny on Her Own

The next concert was scheduled for Utica, New York, and on the day before Jenny and Josephine, Otto and Giovanni, visited Clifton Falls a few miles away. Jenny was like a child again in her delight as she gazed at that curtain of water falling and tumbling over a wall of rocks into the stream below. The road back to town passed through a stretch of forest and she looked around her with a sharp intake of breath. The afternoon sun showing faintly through a tangle of leaves made a design of light and shade on the grass.

"How lovely! How quiet!" Jenny said. "Why don't we stop here for a little while?"

She was humming under her breath as Otto helped her from the carriage. In the dim woods she felt at peace and, seemingly unmindful of her audience, she sat down on a rock and began to sing one of her favorite songs:

> *"Birdling! why is thy heart so blest?*
> *Oh say? Oh, say?*
> *Music o'er flowing from thy breast?*
> *Oh say? Oh say?"*

The last words were a question and, as though in answer, a bird lighted on a bough close by. Its little throat began to

swell as it let out a soft crescendo of sounds. When it fell silent, it cocked its head and looked at Jenny out of beady
black eyes, as though daring her to sing as well. She laughed
softly and took up the challenge:

> *"My heart is full, and yet is light.*
> *My heart is glad in day and night,*
> *Nor know I why I'm singing."*

When she had finished, the bird sang again. In the next
pause, Jenny sang, and waited for his reply. It was almost
like a duet, and the woods seemed filled with music. Otto,
though shaken out of his usual calm, said nothing. Giovanni
was not so reticent.

"*Cara mia!*" he exclaimed, then checked himself. He had
no intention of making such an open display of his feelings
before a young man he persisted in thinking of as a rival.
To cover his confusion, Giovanni's next words were light
and bantering.

"Ah! So your little feathered friend is singing after your
method?"

"No, it is I who sing after *his*," said Jenny seriously. "As
you well know, I sing after no one's method, except that of
the birds, so far as I am able."

The memory of that hour in the quiet woods stayed with
her during the difficult weeks that followed. New York
State was one of the most attractive regions she had yet visited, but the concerts were not going well under the new
management. Max Hjortzberg and Charles Seyton were
young and inexperienced, and receipts began to fall off.
Jenny, anxious as always that the price of admission be kept
at a reasonable figure, had ordered that no seats be sold at
auction. This order was carried out with discouraging results. Speculators, whom the Americans called *sharpies*,
rushed to buy up most of the tickets, then resold them at a

handsome profit. In order to save money, the concerts were given, not in public halls, but in churches. In one town a local man, who lived next door to the church, set up bleachers in his backyard. He charged a dollar admission, and his customers could hear, even if they could not see.

The July nights were warm, and nearly every place where Jenny sang a crowd would gather outside the open windows. Though this nonpaying audience was usually quiet, one night in Albany there was some commotion, and Jenny became frightened. She remembered what had happened in Pittsburgh, and in the middle of the "Casta Diva" she fainted. A doctor was called, who gave her restoratives, and she insisted on finishing the program.

Until then Jenny had not realized what a toll the constant travel and rehearsals had taken of her strength, and her fatigue showed in her voice. There was now no Mr. Barnum to stand between her and a demanding public, and when things went wrong she often was the one who had to take the blame.

Did she miss her "dear Barnum," read one newspaper item, the manager who had always done everything "in the right way, in the right place, at the right time?"

One frequent complaint was about the lack of an orchestra, which prevented the vocalists from performing their more spectacular numbers. The prices charged for tickets caused a great deal of grumbling. Seats in church pews could not be numbered as exactly as in a concert hall, and the audience often felt crowded and uncomfortable. Jenny was harassed by details which had never concerned her before, and her nerves felt raw. When Jules Benedict announced that he must return to England, she broke down and wept.

"I won't leave until after the concerts scheduled for Buffalo," he assured her. "I have been away from my family much too long, and you really do not need a conductor now that you no longer have an orchestra."

Jenny knew he was right, but she would miss his wise counsel.

"Why doesn't our entire troupe take a few days' rest before you sail?" she suggested. "All of us have been under a strain, and I am told that Niagara Falls is near Buffalo. Fröken Bremer was there and she said no one should leave America without seeing them."

At the thought of a holiday, Jenny's eyes brightened, and her enthusiasm was shared by the other members of the company. By the time they reached Buffalo, she felt more like her old self, and she was enchanted by the blue reaches of Lake Erie. Like the ocean, it stretched away toward the horizon, blending into the deeper blue of the sky.

The first time Jenny looked at the lake, it was calm and peaceful, but there was little calm in the city. A fugitive slave had escaped to Buffalo, hoping to find his way to Canada where slavery was unlawful. Unfortunately, he was caught before he could reach the border and was now lodged in a Buffalo jail. According to the Fugitive Slave Act recently passed by the United States Congress, he must be returned to his old master in the South, and a group of indignant citizens was raising a fund to buy his freedom from the man who owned him.

Jenny was puzzled. In Sweden at that time, there were rigid class distinctions, and a poor man had little chance ever to improve his lot. Hundreds of her countrymen had come to America, hoping to find greater freedom and opportunity than would have been possible in the old homeland. Yet in this same America there were slaves.

How could that be? she wondered.

And what about the first Americans? When four Indian chiefs had called on her in Rochester a short time before, she had offered to sing for them. The news had spread, and one morning while she and Otto were rehearsing for the first Buffalo concert, Max knocked on the door. Another group of Indians was waiting downstairs. They had heard of the squaw with a voice like that of the birds that sang in the treetops, and they wanted to hear her.

Jenny had never been called a *squaw* before. She was not quite sure what it meant, but she nodded in agreement. A few minutes later, seven bronze-skinned callers entered her sitting room.

Not a word was spoken as they seated themselves in a circle on the floor. The only one who spoke English was a Mr. Wheelock, whose father had been a white man. His mother had belonged to the Ojibway tribe, he explained, as did his companions, and they came from the far-off Minnesota Territory. Because they felt they had been unjustly treated by the Palefaces, they were on their way to Washington to see the Great White Father.

"You mean the President?" asked Jenny.

She remembered her own visit with President Fillmore, and how impressed she had been by his informality. It seemed even more remarkable that these primitive men from the forests were to have an opportunity to meet the head of a great nation face to face and tell him their troubles. That could never have happened in a European country where rules of court etiquette had to be strictly observed.

After Jenny sang for the Indians, they filed past her to shake hands. She wished all of them well on their mission to Washington, and Mr. Wheelock translated. He thanked her, but the others remained silent, their faces impassive. When at last they strode out into the hall, Jenny turned to Otto.

"We shall probably meet more Indians at Niagara," she told him. "Fröken Bremer said she saw many of them in the woods near the Falls. But come, I have something to show you." A map was spread out on her desk. "See, here is the Niagara River." She traced the line with her finger. "The river leads from Lake Erie where we are now into Lake On-tar-i-o—" She stumbled over the unfamiliar Indian word.

"On the farther shore is Toronto. It is not nearly as far away as I had thought, just a short voyage by steamboat, really. I have received another invitation to give a concert there. The letter is so insistent, and the people seem so hospitable—"

She paused uncertainly. More and more she had been leaning on Otto, depending on him for advice. "What would you think of going to Toronto?"

"But, Fräulein, I thought you intended to take a long holiday," he protested. "You gave us quite a start when you fainted that time in Albany."

"Yes, I am tired, and it is important that I rest my voice. But after a few weeks I should be all right again, and I should like to stay in America a while longer. You know that Mr. Benedict is leaving?"

Otto nodded.

"I have been intending to ask you. If I decide to stay, will you stay with me?"

"Of course, Fräulein." For a young man usually so reticent, the words fairly tumbled over one another. "There is nothing you could ask of me I would not do. Why, ever since I was a boy—I mean since we first met—"

Jenny looked at him, puzzled and alarmed. Having brought her own feelings under control, she must not now allow this young man to get any false ideas. Their relationship must be kept impersonal.

"You are still little more than a boy," she reminded him. "If you agree, I shall write to your parents and assure them that I shall look after your interests."

Otto flushed, and Jenny laid her hand on his arm. She had not meant her words to sound so condescending. "You made a long voyage at my request, and it is only fair that you get something out of it."

Jenny could not quite hide her amusement at Otto's woebegone expression.

"Pray, do not look so sorrowful, my friend. You don't act like a boy. Sometimes I think you are really more like a steady old man."

Otto looked even more uncomfortable. Which was worse —to be called a boy or a steady old man? It was hard to decide. Jenny motioned toward the piano.

"Let us run through the 'Echo Song,'" she said. "Just think! Only two more concerts, then on to Niagara!"

The waters of the Niagara River pouring over steep precipices some twenty miles from Buffalo were the mecca even then for more than sixty thousand tourists every year. This stream formed part of the boundary between the United States and Canada, and Goat Island in the middle of the river divided the rush of waters into two mighty cataracts: the Canadian Falls and the American. Max had engaged rooms at Clifton House on the Canadian side, with a breathtaking view of both Falls. When Jenny and her troupe arrived toward the end of July, they stood on the wide veranda for a long time, drinking in the grandeur of the scene.

The waters were greener than they had expected. The Canadian Falls were like a great smooth sheet of emeralds, until the water dashed against the rocks far below. There it burst into spray, forming a frothy snow-white column rising toward the sky.

"Look! The rainbows!" Belletti exclaimed.

Not one rainbow but several arched over the water, only to appear and disappear as the sunlight shifted.

It was a magnificent sight, but Niagara had many moods.

When the moon rose, the waters were shot through with silver; in the early morning they were a pale blush pink. Later, they seemed to change to molten gold and then to emerald again.

Jenny stepped out on the balcony that opened off her sitting room, the better to listen to the mighty music of the Falls. Reluctantly, she turned to go back inside when she heard a knock at the door.

"Come in," she said, and Giovanni Belletti entered, a newspaper in his hand.

"Believe me, Jenny," he said, "I am not responsible."

"Not responsible for what?"

He handed her the newspaper, and surprise, dismay, and anger showed in quick succession on her face as she read the story:

> *Jenny Lind has made arrangements for a permanent continuance of the "united state." We can state that Signor Belletti is the happy man. Every arrangement, we believe, has been completed for the nuptials of the loving couple.*

Jenny did not dare speak for a moment. When she finally did, she measured each word carefully, as though trying to control her temper.

"I shall ask Max to write to the newspaper at once and insist on a retractment of the story."

"*Certamente!* But I give you my word, I said nothing to any reporter."

"Yet this is not the first time that a newspaper has printed this same rumor. Remember Nashville? And there have been several newspapers since then. Why should reporters think we are to be married, unless you give them that impression?"

"Perhaps I do. It may be that my feeling for you is written on my face whenever we are together."

Jenny turned away from the look of misery in his eyes.

"I wish I could feel differently," she said more gently. "Oh, Giovanni, I don't want to hurt you."

"I know that, *cara mia,* but don't you see that it will be better for both of us if I leave? When Mr. Benedict sails, I shall sail with him."

"Not you, too? How can I get along without you?"

"Señor Salvi is an excellent tenor. Joseph Burke a good violinist. Then you will have Otto."

Jenny ignored the hint of mockery in his voice and outlined her plan. It was unthinkable, she told him, to allow two good friends to cross three thousand miles of ocean without telling them a last goodby. She and Josephine would accompany them to New York. The rest of the troupe, it was decided, would remain at Clifton House.

While in New York, Jenny met Giovanni's younger brother, Enrico, who had recently arrived from Italy. He played the clarinet, and she agreed that he should join the company when it resumed its tour. A few days later he stood beside the two women on the dock at the foot of Canal Street. Jenny's eyes misted as she continued to wave until her friends' ship was a mere dot on the horizon. With a strange empty feeling in her heart, she climbed back into her carriage for the ride back to her hotel.

"Have you forgotten," said Josephine, always practical, "that Mr. Bushnell has an appointment this afternoon?"

No, Jenny had not forgotten. Convinced that many of her difficulties of the past summer were due to inefficiency, she had come to a decision. She needed a man with more experience to oversee the work of Max Hjortzberg and Mr. Seyton. She had confidence in Mr. Bushnell, a former agent for P.T. Barnum. He had agreed to manage any future concerts she might give in America, and the plan was discussed in more detail that afternoon. After he left, Jenny sat down at her desk to compose a letter to Otto's father.

I have sung so much during the last ten months—she wrote—*that it is absolutely necessary for me to rest for several weeks. It is my intention, however, to give more concerts in America later on. I should like, therefore, to propose that Herr Otto Goldschmidt should work with me in any future concerts in this country. Herr Otto has accepted my proposal, and I hope I have not acted against your wishes in keeping him a little longer in America.*

She went on to outline the generous terms she proposed to offer her accompanist. Then she added another sentence. She wanted Otto's parents to know how highly she regarded their son:

He has such a clear insight into everything, and is always guided by such a right and noble feeling that one must respect his judgment.

Jenny reached for a little pot of sand on the desk, took a pinch, and sprinkled it over the page to dry the ink. By the time Josephine returned from posting the letter she was in bed. Since her parting from Giovanni, she felt drained of all emotion.

Had she been foolish to let him go? Had she been foolish to leave Mr. Barnum's management? No, she told herself stubbornly, both decisions had been wise. Or had they? She was so weary of always being alone, of having no one dear and close to her to whom she could turn for advice. Why, why, must she always be so racked by indecision?

She felt no indecision, though, about her return to Niagara. She was glad to be going back, and with this thought she drifted off to sleep.

19 §§

Back to Niagara

On her arrival at the railroad station at Niagara, Jenny could hear the roar of the mighty cataract in the distance. It reminded her of a great orchestral accompaniment, and the road that led to Clifton House was just as she remembered it. Tranquil and peaceful! she thought as she sank back against the cushions of the carriage. It was as Fredrika Bremer had said, she told Josephine. Niagara was "sweet and mighty," both at the same time.

Suddenly the driver drew rein to his horse, bringing the carriage to such an abrupt halt that Jenny was jolted out of her reverie. He had barely missed running down a young man and woman who had emerged from a stretch of woodland to cross the road. Walking hand in hand, they were so absorbed in each other, they had not noticed the approach of the carriage, and not until the driver shouted did they step aside to let it pass.

The driver chuckled. "You can always tell 'em. Just married. Lots of couples come here on their honeymoon."

Jenny smiled politely, but it was a sad smile; there would be no honeymoon for her, here or elsewhere, but when the carriage rounded a bend in the road a few minutes later she almost forgot her feeling of depression. Otto, Joseph Burke, and Señor Salvi were waiting on the hotel veranda, and they rushed down the steps to greet her. In the warmth of their welcome, she felt an abrupt change of mood and entered with enthusiasm into their plans for a week of sightseeing. Each of her friends had some special place he wanted to show her.

Their first excursion was to the American side of Niagara, and from there the Canadian Falls looked even more impressive. The next morning they scrambled down a steep rocky path. Standing on a ledge, they could look *up* at the Falls, and it was both alarming and exhilarating to watch the seething waters rushing and tumbling toward them.

Another day the troupe took a ride on the *Maid of the Mist*. This new little steamer nosed its way into the current of the river, and presently the passengers were enveloped in the spray. They had been given mackintoshes to wear, but Jenny's new bonnet was ruined. She hardly noticed in the excitement of the moment.

"Look!" she said, pointing to a vast curtain of white mist that seemed to shut out the rest of the world. "We are actually *behind* the Falls."

Fortunately for Jenny, most of the other tourists were so intent on sightseeing that she was not always recognized. She visited the shops where beadwork and other handcraft of the Indians of the region were on sale, and took long walks without a crowd following at her heels. She prized each hour of the time left to her before she must begin another concert tour, and only one incident marred her holiday.

It happened one Sunday evening. Seated at the piano in her suite, she was singing a Swedish hymn, not aware that a few guests had gathered in the hall outside to listen. In a sudden gust of wind her candle sputtered and went out, and she stepped to the door to call one of the maids. The music had stopped so abruptly and she opened the door so quickly that one gentleman—who was leaning against it, not wanting to miss a single golden note—practically fell into her arms.

Jenny was indignant. Must she be spied on even here? The man picked himself up and backed away, and in the light from the hallway she saw the startled expression on his face. The rest of her impromptu audience laughed. Later, when Jenny told her friends about the incident, what she chiefly remembered was how her astonished eavesdropper had looked when he made his unexpected plunge into her room. Then she laughed, too.

It was a night not soon forgotten for another reason. Several hours later, Clifton House guests gathered on the veranda to watch the Aurora Borealis, that brilliant display of lights frequently seen in northern countries but of rare occurrence in the United States. The heavens were illuminated with streamers and bands of light, both green and crimson, shifting, quivering, shooting upward toward the middle of the dark sky. There were gasps of amazement from Jenny's friends, and she seemed almost transported with nostalgia.

"Just as in Sweden," she cried. "Oh, I feel so rested, so refreshed, ready for whatever lies ahead."

After two benefits in Buffalo, the next concerts were scheduled for Toronto. Mr. Bushnell and Mr. Seyton left some days in advance of the rest of the party to make final arrangements about the concert hall and the sale of tickets. The troupe began rehearsing, and Jenny looked on her appearance in the Canadian city as a challenge. Recent experience proved that she had owed a great deal to Mr. Barnum's expert management, but her pride was piqued by some of the comments in unfriendly newspapers. She must prove to others and to herself that her early triumphs in America had not been due entirely to his genius for publicity. She had succeeded in Europe without P.T. Barnum's help, and she could do it again, she told herself firmly.

To be sure, the lack of an orchestra was a handicap, but Otto was as skilled an accompanist as she could wish for. Joseph Burke with his violin and young Belletti with his clarinet would add variety to the programs, but she felt vaguely uncomfortable in the latter's company. With his dark burning eyes and handsome face, he was a constant reminder of his brother. She tried not to think about her unhappy friend.

"I can't allow myself to be torn to pieces by doubts," she confided to Josephine. "I must think only of getting ready for this new series of concerts."

She looked forward to her afternoon rehearsals with Otto Goldschmidt, but they felt a mutual restraint in each other's company which she seemed unable to break down. One morning, standing at the window of her room, she could see him pacing back and forth. Impulsively she turned to Margaret, one of the hotel maids, and asked that a picnic lunch be packed for her. A half hour later Jenny rushed downstairs where she found Herr Goldschmidt on the veranda gazing moodily at the falls.

"Otto," she said, "how would you like to hire a boat to take us over to Goat Island for the morning?"

His dark sensitive face lighted with a smile. Jenny did not need to add, "Just the two of us." He knew that was what she meant.

Goat Island was one of the several islands in the river and, in spite of its commonplace name, one of the most beautiful spots in Niagara. Walking along the path that led to the western end of the island, the gleam and glitter of the water could be glimpsed faintly through a tangle of leaves. Then suddenly the water was all around them, and Jenny sank down on a fallen log.

"I am so glad that we . . ."

Otto finished the sentence for her. "That we came alone. I, too, Fräulein."

"You always seem to know what I am going to say before I say it. But I can read your thoughts, too."

"Not all of them," he said gravely.

"Suppose you try me. You begin a sentence."

"Very well. Do you know what the Falls are called
by . . ."

"The Indians?" said Jenny. "Let me think. "The Thunder of Waters'?"

"You're close. The name I heard was 'Thunderer of
Waters.' "

"Oh, Otto, I never want to leave. I could stay here forever. Fröken Bremer once said she always felt the Falls
were trying to tell her something."

"I know what they tell me. They say the world is beautiful, but that I know already. It is beautiful because you—"

Jenny hastily changed the subject, and for the next few
minutes she was very busy unpacking the picnic basket. By
now she felt certain that Otto returned her love, or thought
he did; but she must not let him say what she most wanted
to hear. She already had hurt Giovanni, and she did not
want to hurt Otto, too. Not him of all people! She must
never allow a conversation to reach a point where he might
ask her to marry him. With the difference in their ages she
must be sensible for both of them.

Otto, though, had no intention of proposing. He was
comparatively unknown. Jenny Lind was one of the most
famous women in the world, and he felt it would be presumptuous to suggest that she might be his wife. Jenny
seemed to read what was in his mind, and an uncomfortable
silence fell between them. All the joy had gone out of their
picnic, and they said very little as they ate their lunch. Neither was any good at small talk, and in silence they finally
made their way through the woods. The boat was waiting
at the end of the path to take them back to the Canadian
shore.

Jenny had hardly reached her room, when Margaret, the maid, knocked on the door.

"I have come to say goodby, Miss Lind. I am leaving tomorrow to be married."

"Married? Would you mind if I came?"

Margaret seemed overwhelmed. "Would you, Miss Lind? I have no family or friends close by."

"Then it is settled. If you will allow me, I would like to be your attendant, your bridesmaid."

Looking over her extensive wardrobe, Jenny found a white dress and gloves for the bride to wear. For a wedding present she gave her a fan and a handsome brooch. Margaret tried on the dress and could hardly believe her good fortune when she looked at her reflection in the mirror. Her eyes were glowing.

"What will my Jim say when he sees me?" she exclaimed. "Jim Copeland is the young man I am going to marry. He hasn't any folks either and—"

"Then he must have a groomsman," Jenny interrupted. "I am sure Mr. Goldschmidt would be glad to stand up with him."

Early the next morning two carriages left the hotel for the town of Lewiston a few miles away. Jenny and Margaret rode in the first, Otto and Jim Copeland in the second. Jenny's heart was beating as fast as that of the bride by the time they entered the little Episcopal church and, listening to the solemn words of the marriage ceremony, she had to blink back the tears. She did not need to look at Otto to know that he, too, was deeply moved.

Back in her hotel suite, her thoughts were in turmoil again. Otto had all the qualities she would ever want in a husband. Unlike Giovanni, he was never jealous. He had the refinement and genius that had once drawn her to Adolf Lindblad. He had Julius Gunther's charm, but in the end would she be able to make him happy? Might not the difference in their ages always stand between them?

She kept asking herself this question again and again, and because she was worried and unhappy she was sometimes curt with Otto during rehearsals. Yet he never seemed to take offense. He was always patient, always kind. She wondered if he was asking himself the same question, but he was more in control of his emotions than she could ever hope to be. Finally in desperation, Jenny wrote Judge Munthe, her guardian, in Sweden.

> *Herr Otto Goldschmidt is the first person I feel I am really made for. He can fulfill all the needs of my soul. We are made of the same stuff, and one needs only to begin a sentence before the other knows the end of it. But—he is so young. . . Isn't this cruel? Isn't this absolutely desperate!—No one has ever existed or can exist with whom I can live as* one *soul and* one *heart as with Otto. But age! age!*

She gave Judge Munthe a list of the towns on the itinerary Mr. Bushnell had worked out for the coming tour. She begged her guardian to write as soon as possible.

> *Send me some soothing words in reply to this*—she added—*and give me something like advice or dissuasion.*

During the next few weeks she was to wait anxiously for a reply that did not come.

Triumph in Toronto

Since coming to America Jenny Lind had traveled by river steamer, train, and stagecoach, but the short trip on October 20 alongside the Niagara River provided a new experience. Because of the Falls, the river that connected Lake Erie and Lake Ontario was not navigable for several miles, and it was necessary to ride in the horsedrawn cars of the Erie and Ontario Railway. The cars, like other trains, ran on tracks, but were pulled not by a steam engine but by two stout horses. Passengers were accommodated on hard wooden benches, but Jenny almost forgot her discomfort when she turned and looked through the window. The maple trees had turned scarlet, sumac blazed in fence corners, and the branches of the oak trees dripped with golden leaves.

"America in October!" she exclaimed. "You missed it last year, Otto. I am so glad you could join the company in time—"

She paused and he finished the sentence. "This year so we can share it together. Indeed, Fräulein, I too am glad. We have nothing like it in Europe."

"No, in Europe the leaves usually just wither and die. Here they indulge in a last glorious fling of color."

The bright autumn scenery and the novelty of the ride made the time pass quickly. Sooner than the passengers would have thought possible, they were looking on another great inland sea, Lake Ontario. The boat, *Chief Justice*, was tied up at the dock, and Captain Miller who was in command of the vessel assured Jenny and her troupe that they were only a few hours sail from Toronto. He would wait there to bring them back when the concerts were over.

The vessel, though much smaller, recalled pleasant memories of the *Atlantic* in which Jenny had crossed to America. She stood at the railing, straining her eyes for her first glimpse of Toronto. In the distance she could make out the dim outlines of a lighthouse and then a few church spires. A closer view showed wide straight streets set at right angles to the lake. With its handsome buildings, Toronto was an impressive city but not quite what Jenny had expected. She had thought Canadian cities might be more like those in Europe, with narrow crooked streets.

"That is true of Quebec and Montreal," the captain told her, "but they were founded many years ago. Toronto is a much newer city, and visitors from the States often tell us it has a 'Yankee' look about it."

When the *Chief Justice* dropped anchor at Queen's Wharf, Jenny saw a group of distinguished-looking gentlemen at the foot of the gangplank. The mayor was waiting to shake hands, and he introduced the other members of the city council.

"Toronto welcomes you, Miss Lind," said the mayor. "It is generous of you to donate the profits from your second concert to some of our local charities. As a small token of our gratitude, you and the members of your company are invited to be the guests of the city while you are here."

"You are very kind," said Jenny in surprise.

Since leaving Mr. Barnum's management, she had been accustomed to paying her own expenses.

"The tickets for both concerts have all been sold,"

the mayor went on. "Hundreds of our citizens must be turned away without having an opportunity to hear you."

"If you wish," Jenny offered, "I shall be glad to give a third concert, provided that the profits from it can also go to charity."

The mayor helped his famous guest into the first of several carriages lined up on the wharf. He sat beside her on the ride to Ellah House, where rooms had been reserved. King Street was lined by cheering crowds, and Jenny waved and smiled. The smile grew tender when the mayor told her that the ladies of Toronto were raising funds to build a much-needed orphans' home. A good part of Miss Lind's generous donation would be used for that.

"Nothing could make me happier," she replied, "than to have my donation used for the children. It was to help the youth of my own country that I undertook this trip to America."

The concerts were held in St. Lawrence Hall, a handsome building recently completed. The first night, considered the most brilliant social event of the season, was well patronized by the people Mr. Barnum would have called "the fashionables." Gentlemen in broadcloth and wide silk cravats doffed their high plush hats and escorted ladies in rustling silks down the aisles. Jewels sparkled under the magnificent chandelier that lighted the hall. There was a low, expectant buzz of conversation, which changed into applause that rocked the building when Herr Goldschmidt led Miss Lind toward the footlights.

After several weeks' absence from the concert stage, Jenny felt even more than the usual trepidation when she began her first number. This was a selection from *The Daughter of the Regiment*, Donizetti's opera in which she had scored one of her greatest triumphs, and after the first few notes she was herself again. Out of courtesy to the many residents of Toronto, whose forebears had come from

Scotland, she had decided to end her program with two Scottish ballads, "John Anderson, my Jo," and "Comin' Through the Rye."

But these numbers were not the end. Jenny received such an ovation it seemed that her charmed listeners would never let her go. Again and again she came before the footlights in response to the applause, and as a final encore she chose the British national anthem, "God Save the Queen."

Like Americans south of the border, her Canadian admirers were impressed, not only by the prima donna's voice, but by the woman herself. The next day, a Toronto newspaper pointed out that her feeling for "the sufferings and misfortunes of her fellow creatures" was all the more remarkable because she had been the object of so much praise and adulation.

"Every city through which she has passed," the story continued, "can bear witness to her generosity. Even here in Toronto, unknown and uninterested in our affairs, she drops in among us and freely gives five hundred pounds to our charities, a sum which could not be collected for any one benevolent enterprise from all our wealthy citizens put together! Truly such a woman is one of the mysteries of the human race."

Jenny was accustomed to extravagant praise and professed to be annoyed by it. Though she was sincere in this, deep in her heart she felt a sense of failure when the praise was lacking. Because she was deeply sensitive about some of the newspaper comments since she had left Mr. Barnum, it was natural she should feel all the more gratified by her triumph in Toronto.

It had been arranged that after the third concert, the members of the troupe were to be driven directly to the Queen's Wharf where they would board the *Chief Justice*. On that final night, Jenny noticed that the entire gallery was occupied by men in the uniform of Scottish High-

landers. She had heard that the 71st Regiment was in Toronto, and she was pleased that they had decided to attend
in a body.

Jenny was even more pleased at the end of the concert,
to find the regiment waiting outside the hall. The horses
had been unhitched from her carriage, and several young
men stood ready to pull it through the streets. An officer
stepped forward, and requested that she permit them that
pleasure.

"Why, thank you," said Jenny.

The years seemed to drop away as her thoughts went
back to a night in Hamburg when a group of students after
a performance had shown their appreciation by drawing
her carriage through the streets. Otto also remembered that
night, for he had been one of the students. Jenny thanked
the Scottish officer, then gestured for Otto and Salvi to
share the carriage with her.

Otto shook his head. This honor was intended for Jenny
Lind alone; he and the other musicians would follow in a
second carriage. The regimental band, playing military airs,
led the way through the streets to the Queen's Wharf.
After Captain Miller escorted Jenny up the gangplank, she
stood by the railing and waved to the enthusiastic young
Scots gathered on the wharf below. The band continued
to play as the engines churned and the boat nosed its way
out into the dark waters. Even when Jenny could no
longer see the musicians, the strains of "Auld Lang Syne"
could be heard faintly in the distance.

Shortly after the return to Buffalo, the troupe took passage on a Lake Erie steamer for Cleveland. Mr. Bushnell
had arranged for concerts at several places in Ohio and
Pennsylvania. A swing back east, by way of Philadelphia
and New York, brought Jenny to Boston, her favorite
city. Then to New York again in time for Christmas. Her
agents informed the newspapers that her farewell concert

was scheduled for December 31. She would then disband her company and return to Europe.

It was a quiet Christmas. Jenny and Josephine spent most of the day in their hotel suite, but Otto came to share their holiday dinner in the public dining room. He seemed unusually quiet. Obviously, he had made up his mind to be sensible about her, and she must be sensible about him. Two and a half months had passed since she had asked her guardian's advice, and she felt hurt that he had never replied. Perhaps his silence was a reply, and Judge Munthe considered her question one that only she could answer. Or perhaps he remembered her experience with Captain Harris and thought she was repeating the same mistake in considering marriage to a younger man. In that case, the judge, who was always kind, would be reluctant to cause her pain.

Jenny was in her dressing room at the theater a few days later, waiting for Otto to come and rehearse, when a letter from Judge Munthe finally came. Glancing at the date, she saw that it had been more than a month on the way, and she was almost afraid to read it. Hearing Otto's knock, she called, "Come in," in a voice she could not keep from trembling. Her back was to the door, but he saw her face in the mirror. The tears were coursing down her cheeks. Otto seemed to cross the room in a single stride.

"What is it, Jenny? What is wrong?"

"This—this letter, and to think I never knew, that I could not be there."

"Knew what, Liebchen?"

He hardly seemed aware of the affectionate name he had called her, and he gripped the back of her chair so hard that his knuckles showed white.

"My mother—oh, Otto, now at last when everything was nice and smooth between us, she is dead. And my poor father. What will my father do?"

She broke down and the words came in a rush. About her unhappy childhood with her mother and her disillusionment about her father whom she had once adored. Though Jenny, as soon as she could earn enough money, had provided them with every comfort in a little house of their own, she had wanted to do much more. Now that Fru Lind was quieter and more reasonable, Jenny had hoped they could spend more time together in the kind of home for which she had always yearned. She had wanted so desperately for her mother to love her just for herself. She had wanted to return that love and make Fru Lind's old age a time of joy and peace and tender care. Now it was too late.

Otto, who had been brought up in a family where there was warmth and understanding, was appalled. In spite of their little game of finishing each other's sentences, of reading each other's thoughts, this was his first inkling of Jenny's utter loneliness of spirit. It occurred to him that even a very famous woman could need help, that she could need love.

If only—he thought miserably.

Already ashamed of her outburst, Jenny dried her eyes. Glancing into the mirror she could see Otto's face. She could read the indecision. He was still in awe of her, and at that moment she would gladly have changed places with the maid who had served her breakfast that morning. Otto would have given anything not to be so young, a fact of which Jenny had too often reminded him.

"If only—" This time he said the words out loud.

"Otto," she replied, "it does not matter. You are old and wise beyond your years."

She reached back and took his hand, laying it against her hot cheek. This might not be considered proper behavior for a young woman of 1852, but being sensible was no longer important. Afterward, she could not quite remember exactly what was said.

Did Otto ask her to marry him? Or did she have to ask him? At the moment there was no need for words.

21 §§

Paradise Revisited

When Jenny confided to Josephine that she and Otto were to be married, her long-time companion merely smiled.

"I thought this might happen."

"Aren't you surprised?" Jenny demanded. "I myself never expected it. You know how afraid I have been of marrying a man younger than I am. After I broke with Claudius, I declared I never would."

Suddenly she stopped. It seemed almost a sacrilege to mention Captain Harris in the same breath with Otto.

"For that matter," she went on, "I thought I was never going to marry at all, but Josephine, I have been with Otto under the most trying circumstances. Of all the men I have known he is the most gentle and unselfish, the noblest, the most reasonable—"

She paused. There were not enough words to express how she felt about Otto. It was so easy to confide in him. Her feeling as a child that she was not wanted, her shock at fourteen when she learned that her parents were not married and her disappointment in her father seemed to recede into the shadows when Otto put his arms around her. Her father must be provided for, of course, and he helped her to compose a letter to Judge Munthe. Her guardian was asked to find a family with whom her father could live and who would see to his comfort. The problem seemed easier because Otto had helped her to solve it.

"Oh, Josephine," Jenny said aloud, "you know how difficult it has been for me to be alone. All my life I have yearned for a real home. You don't think I am unfair to Otto, do you, to let him marry me when I am so much older?"

"Certainly not. It has been obvious to everyone that he has been in love with you all along."

"Yes," said Jenny dreamily, "he told me so himself. Ever since he met me six years ago, and I didn't know. Of course, it would be better if he were not so much younger. But I shall try to make him as happy as he will make me."

"You will," Josephine assured her. "You would have realized that long ago if you hadn't been so—"

"So stubborn? Perhaps, but you know what I have said —'All makes at last for good.'"

Except for Josephine, the engagement was a well-kept secret. Because of her mother's death the farewell concert was canceled, and Jenny was grateful that she was not besieged for interviews.

It seems hard—read one newspaper account—*to part with the fair and generous Swede without saying farewell. This closing concert had been counted on by many. But we will respect the sanctity of sorrow and bid her a mute adieu, trusting that time will heal her sorrow and that her peerless voice is not yet lost to the world. May we even hope that we shall hear her again in America?*

When Jenny Lind decided to return to Boston, instead of sailing for Liverpool, it was assumed that she needed a rest. Though that was true, no one suspected her real reason. She wanted to be married in Boston, and there was only one place where she wished to spend her honeymoon. Not Niagara, which was supposed to be a haven for newly married couples, but in Northampton. It was in this peaceful New England village that her true feelings for Otto had first been revealed to her, though at the time her love had seemed hopeless.

On her arrival at Revere House in Boston, Jenny's old rooms were made ready for her, and she and Josephine felt they were coming home. Otto took a room close by, and a few of Jenny's old friends were taken into their confidence. She took Otto to Cambridge to call on Professor Longfellow, and she was much gratified just before she left when he drew her to one side.

"He is a good man, Miss Lind," he said. "A good man."

When Mrs. Samuel Ward heard the news, she insisted that the couple must be married at the Ward home on Beacon Hill, and the date was set for February 5. That matter settled, Jenny and Otto took a train for Northampton, where they engaged a suite at the Round Hill Hotel. The rooms were furnished, but Jenny informed the manager that she intended to bring her own silver and linens, and her own kitchen utensils. Since this was to be her first real home, even though it was a temporary one, she wanted to prepare for it as would any bride.

With less than a month to get ready, January sped by in a flurry of shopping. Fortunately, Jenny's movements were not followed as closely in the press as might have happened if she had been giving concerts. Sometimes, with her veil pulled down over her face against the biting wind, she was not even recognized as she crossed the Common with Josephine or Otto. The two women shopped for all manner of useful articles, and Jenny showed the same pride in an iron skillet she selected as in some of the costly jewels that had been presented to her in bygone days by monarchs in Europe.

It was Otto who accompanied her to a silversmith's.

"Herr Goldschmidt," she told the proprietor of the shop, "has kindly offered to give me his opinion on some flat silver."

Each time a new design was being considered, she turned to Otto for advice, and when the choice was finally made she ordered the flatware engraved.

"J—" she began.

"Not J.L.?" the proprietor asked.

"No, just *J* encircled by an *O*."

At his look of surprise, she added with a smile, "You see, I am just a cipher."

"Very well, Mademoiselle."

The proprietor was puzzled, but if that was what the prima donna wanted, that was what she must have. Jenny could hardly keep from giggling as they left the shop. Her secret was safe; the silversmith had not realized that Herr Goldschmidt's first name was Otto. But he had not recognized Otto's last name, either, and that was a disturbing thought. Would it be that way after their marriage? Would her husband always have to take second place?

"Liebchen," he told her, "you must never say that again."

Jenny looked at him in surprise.

"Say what?" she asked.

"Call yourself a cipher."

"Why not? There is nothing I want as much to be Madame Goldschmidt."

"Then we must compromise on Madame Lind-Goldschmidt. You can never belong only to me, Liebchen. You could not stop being Jenny Lind, even if you wanted to."

Jenny smiled up at him gratefully. Perhaps Otto understood her better than she understood herself, and of course he was right. She could not live without her music. But in the home that they would make together, she wanted him to feel that he would always come first. She hoped he understood the special symbolism of the design she had chosen for their silver. As he helped her across the street, his reassuring pressure on her elbow made her realize that he did.

The wedding day dawned on a city under a blanket of snow, and Jenny's cheeks were tingling with cold as Otto helped her into the sleigh. This sleigh had replaced the carriage in which they had ridden the first time she showed him Beacon Hill, and the sleighbells tinkled softly as the horse climbed the cobbled streets that led to Louisburg Square. Snow was piled high against the iron fence that enclosed the square, and the bare branches of the elm trees now sheathed in ice, glittered in the winter sunshine. The driver brought the horse to a halt before a high prim red brick house, and in the paneled hall Mr. and Mrs. Ward waited to extend a welcome.

A hasty glance into the parlor assured Jenny that the guests had arrived. Just a few friends, including the Honorable Edward Everett, who had been Jenny's host at the Harvard Observatory more than a year earlier. She recalled the brilliant meteor that had flashed across the sky the very moment when she looked through the telescope. An omen of a successful concert tour, her friends had said. Now she was convinced that it had been an omen of the greater happiness that was to come.

It was a simple wedding, with Lily Ward, the small daughter of the household, acting as Jenny's only attendant. The Reverend John Wainwright performed the ceremony. He was the same clergyman who had previously baptized Otto. Though he had grown up in a Jewish home, Otto and Jenny had reasoned that to share the same faith would be an added bond in their life together.

How happy that decision had made her! How lovely she looked in her traditional Swedish bridal gown of white muslin! Her face was radiant under the white veil held in place

Jenny Lind and Otto Goldschmidt, from a daguerreotype taken in Boston before their marriage there in 1852.

Courtesy of The New York Historical Society, New York City.

Miniature ivory head of Jenny Lind.

Courtesy of the Museum of the City of New York.

Left: *No. 20 Louisburg Square (second house from the corner), Beacon Hill, Boston, where Jenny Lind and Otto Goldschmidt were married.*

Courtesy of the New York Historical Society, New York City.

Below: *Round Hill Hotel, Northampton, Massachusetts, where Jenny Lind and Otto Goldschmidt spent their honeymoon. It is the site of the present Clark School for the Deaf.*

Courtesy Forbes Library, Northampton, Massachusetts.

by a crown of orange blossoms intertwined with myrtle. To most people Jenny Lind was beautiful only when she sang, but when she turned to her husband after the ceremony, she knew that to him she would be beautiful at all times. She saw the assurance in the glow of his dark eyes; she felt it in his kiss.

During the reception the guests filed slowly past the bridal couple to offer congratulations and good wishes. It was a very dignified occasion, with each of the gentlemen planting a decorous kiss on Jenny's brow. Finally she could stand it no longer. In an exuberance of feeling she threw her arms around a tall bearded man at the end of the line and gave him an old fashioned Swedish hug. He looked startled but pleased, and after that everyone began to unbend. Jenny Lind was no longer just a famous guest. She was a bride whose happiness was overflowing. Otto stood with his arm around her shoulder. He was fairly beaming with happiness and pride.

Almost before the last guest had departed from Beacon Hill, the news had spread through Boston. That evening a band gathered outside the Ward home to serenade the couple, but they had already departed for Northampton. On reaching the Round Hill Hotel, Otto insisted that he needed no servant to help with the luggage, and he and his bride climbed the stairs alone. In silence they stood outside the door of their suite; it was a moment to be savored. Jenny drew closer to her husband. Otto fitted the key into the lock, and they went inside together.

A few days later Jenny was seated at the desk in the sitting room of their suite. She had letters to write, thanking well-wishers, some of whom she had never met, for wedding presents. Her favorite gift was from Mrs. Samuel Ward—a gold locket containing small portraits of the two Americans she most admired, General Washington and Senator Webster. When she finished her letter to her friend in Louisburg Square, she signed it with a flourish: *Jenny Goldschmidt (doesn't that look prettier?)*.

Then she turned to the pile of newspapers that had accumulated since their arrival at Round Hill. Her marriage to Otto had been one of the scoops of the year, and she could not help feeling somewhat smug that they had been able to keep their engagement a secret. As one of the reporters had expressed it, the Nightingale could afford to *smile in her honeymoon cage at their despair.*

Picking up another newspaper, Jenny laughed out loud.

The Queen of Song Has Committed Matrimony

the headline read. But a third account brought a mist to her eyes:

> *The next song of the Nightingale will, of course, be "Home Sweet Home." May she live a thousand years and sing it every day.*

She glanced at the plain gold band on her hand as she walked over to the window. From there she could look down on several children shouting and sliding on snowy slopes. Green lawns lay buried under an expanse of shining white. White houses nestled under snowladen roofs. More than ever, Northampton seemed "the Paradise of America."

Was it only last July that she had visited it for the first time? Seven months had passed since the night of the storm when she had seen into her own heart. And after that? Why had both of them hesitated for so long?

Oh, Otto! she thought. She had found him late—but not too late.

Her thoughts flashed back to Giovanni Belletti. The catch in his voice when he told her goodby was not easily forgotten, but it was fortunate for both of them that she had resisted his pleas. The last time she had heard from him, he was singing in London, and now he had no Jenny Lind to usurp the limelight. It was so different with Otto. There was no jealousy between them. He wanted her success. She wanted his.

"What are you thinking, Liebchen?"

Otto had entered and was standing behind her, his face buried in her bright hair. What could she answer? The years would not be long enough to tell him all that lay within her heart. She turned and looked into those wise dark eyes.

"Of many things," she said, "but of this, most of all. May God give every married life such true happiness as we now have."

As they lingered on their honeymoon, spring came to Northampton. Jenny rearranged the furniture in their suite, thinking forward to the day when she would furnish a house of their own. In the evening Otto liked to read aloud, while she sat beside the fireplace, her hands busy with her knitting. They talked often of the other musicians in her company who had returned to Europe. Only the genial violinist, Joseph Burke, was still in the States.

In the afternoons Jenny and Otto took long walks, enjoying the green glory of a New England spring. Sometimes she walked alone while her husband practiced. It was a source of pride to Northampton that Madame Lind-Goldschmidt should have chosen this town for her honeymoon. One neighbor grew accustomed to having Jenny stop by to exchange a greeting or to offer a flower. Sometimes she stepped inside to rest. As she held the neighbor's small boy on her lap, her thoughts leaped a span of years. She intended to have a whole houseful of children.

One day her hostess invited her to come for supper. Jenny

accepted on the condition that she not be treated as a guest. When the family rose from the table, she said:

"I know that the children like to play games in the evening and that you have work to do. And so"—she opened her bag triumphantly—"I have brought my knitting."

Such small homely joys! How fitting, she thought, walking back to the hotel beside her husband, that she should find them at last in this little country paradise.

She soon came to realize, though, that Northampton was a paradise with a serpent. Even in her retreat on Round Hill, ugly rumors began to reach her about Otto: he was a fortune hunter who had married a rich prima donna for her money; he cared little for his older wife, except to advance his own career. None of the gossip took into consideration the fact that he was well-to-do in his own right; that he was selfless in his devotion. People who resented his good fortune were only too willing to spread such rumors, and they had small regard for truth.

The first hint that Jenny had of what was being said was a newspaper clipping sent to her by some anonymous person. She threw it away, so Otto would not see it; but she had to talk to someone. That afternoon when she passed by her neighbor's house, there were angry tears in her eyes.

"Someone has said that Otto is not good to me," she sputtered. "Why should anyone try to do him harm—my sweet kind husband?"

The neighbor nodded sympathetically, as Jenny struggled to regain her self-control.

"It is not only that I love him," she went on defiantly, "I am proud of him, too. He is a fine composer as well as a pianist."

Turning abruptly, she continued her walk up the hill. It is not right, she thought, that when we go about people should say, "There is Jenny Lind with her husband." They *should* say, "There is Mr. Goldschmidt with his wife."

Indignant words! She would think and say them often in the years ahead.

She found distraction in a new book which Otto began that evening. The bookseller in Northampton said everyone was talking about it. It was a novel by Harriet Beecher Stowe: *Uncle Tom's Cabin.*

"Is it about slavery?" Jenny asked. "Fröken Bremer said that she would like to write such a book; but she thought that it should be written by an American mother."

And now an American mother had completed just such a story as Fredrika Bremer had in mind. Indeed, Mrs. Stowe had been hard at work on it at the time Fredrika was discussing her own idea with Jenny in Cuba.

Otto opened the book and began to read:

> *One chilly day in February, two gentlemen were sitting in a well-furnished room, in a Kentucky town, discussing some subject with great earnestness. . . . I am sorry to part with Tom,"* [said Mr. Shelby]. . . .

The reading continued far beyond the usual bedtime. The longer Jenny stayed in America, the more perplexed she was about the problem that threatened to tear the nation apart. The Negroes she had seen during her travels in the South had not seemed unhappy. But in Springfield the summer before a leading citizen had confided that his home was a "station" in the "Underground Railroad." He was constantly helping slaves to escape to Canada—men and women who hid by day and traveled by night, risking their lives that they might be free. Surely they had not been happy. Nor had the fugitive slave in Buffalo been happy. Contented people do not try to run away.

"Oh, must you stop now," asked Jenny, when Otto closed the book.

He pointed to the clock on the mantel. But the next evening, and the next, the reading continued. He and his wife shared in the suspense of Eliza's flight across the frozen river and the heroic martyrdom of Uncle Tom.

"Fröken Bremer was right," Jenny said huskily. "It is a book that needed to be written.

Otto nodded, meanwhile leafing through the pages.

"There was a word I did not understand," he said. "Here it is. *Humbug.* Do you know what it means, Jenny?"

Jenny put her finger to her cheek; the word had a familiar ring.

"I remember now," she said. "People used to call Mr. Barnum a humbug, and he never seemed to mind."

She went over and sat on the arm of her husband's chair.

"I wonder if we shall see Mr. Barnum again before we sail. Oh, Otto—"

They had not yet decided where they were to live but it did not matter as long as she was with her husband.

"Only think," she said softly. "When we sail, we shall be going home. We shall be going home together."

22 §§

"All That My Heart . . ."

To Jenny it was unthinkable that they return to Europe on any ship except the *Atlantic*, and their passage had been booked for late May. The plan was to give three farewell concerts in New York. These were to be positively the *only* concerts before their departure, but Jenny and Otto had not counted on the persistence of their new friends. Northampton held such a special place in their hearts that they could not refuse. The benefit recital which took place May 6 in the Town Hall was Jenny's first public appearance as Madame Goldschmidt.

She would never forget Northampton, thought Jenny, as the train pulled out of the station a few days later. She squeezed her husband's arm. She relaxed in the warmth of his smile, as they savored together every memory of the past four months.

Six hours later they emerged into the noise and bustle of New York City, and the idyllic surroundings of Round Hill seemed far away. Again, there were crowds waiting under her hotel window, following her carriage, dogging her footsteps. The crowds were not so large as in the days when Mr. Barnum had pulled the strings, but they were just as demanding. To her surprise she found that she did not mind as much as she once had. With Otto beside her, she was not quite so tense under the strain of rehearsals.

On May 17, a notice appeared in the New York newspapers:

> *Madame Otto Goldschmidt (late M'lle. Jenny Lind) begs to announce that she will give her last concert but two on Tuesday evening. . . .*

There was to be a new assistant soloist. A new conductor had been engaged for the eighty-piece orchestra, but Joseph Burke had arrived to take his old familiar place as concertmaster. Jenny's first recital and a second one a few days later filled every seat in Metropolitan Hall.

When seats for the farewell concert in Castle Garden went on sale in a Broadway music store, hundreds of would-be purchasers lined up outside. A few rowdies in the throng elbowed their way to the front of the line, and after each buying a few tickets entered the line several more times. To Jenny's agent inside the store some of the faces had a too-familiar look. He had an uneasy feeling that he had seen them before, but the line was moving too fast for him to be sure. By three o'clock that afternoon seven thousand tickets had been sold.

It soon became obvious that many of them had been bought by speculators. When Otto arrived on the scene he found them seated on casks outside the music store brazenly offering their tickets for sale. Seats for which they had paid a dollar were sold for three times that amount. Three-dollar tickets went for five.

Jenny would be furious—and rightly so, thought Otto as he entered the store. Many people of moderate means who might otherwise have attended would be unable to afford the inflated prices. The excessive profits would go, not to the fund Jenny was raising for her scholarships, but to a few greedy men.

"Mr. Goldschmidt, I believe."

Otto turned at the sound of a voice at his elbow and bowed. The man, a well-known broker in New York, introduced himself as Mr. Howard.

"I was told that I would find you here," he went on. "I am anxious to obtain two tickets for my wife and a friend who is visiting us."

"I am sorry," Otto replied in his slow, accented English. "All seats have been sold."

Mr. Howard's face clouded. "I am sorry to hear that. Mrs. Stowe will be very disappointed."

"Mrs. Stowe? Harriet Beecher Stowe?"

"Yes. She is our guest. She so much wanted to hear Madame Goldschmidt sing."

"Will you kindly wait here?" Otto's voice quickened with excitement. "Indeed, Mrs. Stowe shall have a seat, whatever happens."

He hurried off to his hotel. In a few minutes he was back. From his pocket he took an envelope addressed to Mrs. Stowe in Jenny's round firm handwriting.

Again he bowed. "With the compliments of Madame Lind-Goldschmidt."

Jenny had set aside a few tickets for the use of personal friends, and the envelope contained tickets for two of the best seats in the house. She had been touched and pleased to learn that the author of the book which had moved her so deeply wished to hear her sing.

The gift was received with something like awe. Fame had come suddenly to the small frail woman responsible for *Uncle Tom's Cabin.* Until her host placed the envelope in her hand, she had no inkling that the name of Harriet Beecher Stowe wielded an influence comparable to that of Jenny Lind. The concert itself, she later described as "a bewildering dream of sweetness and beauty."

Among the thousands in the audience were many who were not so much bewildered as curious. When Jenny's husband led her toward the footlights, there was a general craning of necks to see what manner of man it was who had finally caged the Swedish Nightingale. Mr. Goldschmidt was an amiable young man, good-looking in a quiet way. His talent, his fine musicianship were highly respected—by other musicians.

Why then should there have been a murmur, almost of regret, before the audience broke into applause? If Otto noticed, he gave no sign. As the husband of one of the world's most famous women, he was beginning to learn what it was to be the target of envy and suspicion. He knew that he lacked Jenny's fire, that intangible quality possessed by only a few people in the course of a generation. He also knew that he was needed, and his love was above jealousy. He gave his wife's hand a reassuring squeeze before he seated himself at the piano.

Jenny, looking out into the vast reaches of Castle Garden, realized that she was standing on the same spot where she had made her debut in America. Again she was opening the concert with her favorite aria, the "Casta Diva." For those who had been present on that first momentous night the clock had been turned backward. As before, they thrilled to the pure timber of her notes, her remarkable crescendos, the incredible volume of sound diminishing to a whisper that reached the highest seat in the top gallery. Each number brought thunders of applause. Showers of bouquets were tossed on the stage, and Jenny was caught up in the old heady excitement as she made her low deep curtsy.

She took her final bow with her husband. Otto's solos at the piano had been well received. She did not believe she had ever heard him play with a surer touch. Her pride in him, his pride in her, their mutual love had made better artists of them both; of that she was confident. Certainly she was not the same frightened girl who had come close to breaking down at that first Castle Garden concert twenty months before. The clock had not been turned back for her.

A few minutes later she did have a brief sensation of having stepped into the past. There was a knock on her dressing-room door, a brisk rapping with the knuckles which she would recognize anywhere. A tall stout man entered. Jenny rose and went to meet him with outstretched hands.

"Ah, Mr. Barnum!" She smiled up into the shrewd blue eyes.

"Madame Goldschmidt!"

The unfamiliar title did not come easily, but Jenny was pleased. Too many people forgot and called her Miss Lind. As P.T. Barnum stood looking down at her, he wondered at his own daring. By his own adroit methods—to which she had objected so strenuously on occasion—he had presented her to a vast public whose idea of musical entertainment was a minstrel show. Jenny, bless her, had done the rest. She had enchanted her audiences, and he had lined his pockets.

What even Barnum did not realize was that he had enabled the American people to discover in themselves a taste for good music. Jenny Lind had set the fashion for bringing great musicians to our shores. Opera houses were even then being planned for New York, Boston, and Philadelphia.

"Well, Jenny—"

For the second time since she had known him, he seemed at a loss for words.

"I suppose this is goodby."

She drew him over to a sofa and sat down beside him.

"Mr. Barnum," she blurted out, "when you were my manager, I listened to some bad advice. Now I regret it. I found it very annoying to give concerts on my own account. People cheated me and swindled me very much."

He smiled at her reassuringly. One of her endearing traits was her complete honesty.

"What are your plans when you return to Europe?" he asked.

"I shall probably retire." A wistful note crept into her voice. "I doubt if I shall sing much in public, if at all."

"Retire? If you no longer need large sums—"

Jenny shook her head. She had as much money as she could ever want, and the goal which had brought her to America had been realized.

"There are always people in need," Mr. Barnum continued, "and your heart beats for the poor. How can you say that you will never sing again?"

"You are right," Jenny agreed solemnly. "I shall probably go on singing as long as I have a voice, but it will be mostly for charity."

Barnum repressed a chuckle. Jenny Lind might think she would retire, but she could no more stop singing than she could stop breathing.

Otto came in to say goodby. He slipped an arm around his wife as they stood in the doorway watching Mr. Barnum make his way through the wings. He turned to raise his hand in a last salute. Never had she looked so happy, he thought. She would have been known and loved if she had never sung a note.

"I hope there will be no more goodbys," said Jenny wearily.

Now that the challenge of the final concert had been met, she was suddenly very tired.

"There won't be, my love," Otto replied. "With the *Atlantic* sailing on Friday, there will be no time to receive callers."

Jenny liked the growing tone of authority in his voice. It did not come easily to him, but he knew it was what Jenny wanted. None was so strong as the gentle, she thought

once more *gaze on that sweet landscape where I was so
happy*.

This letter was written from Dresden, but after six years
in Germany the Goldschmidts made their permanent home
in England. Here two sons, Walter and Ernest, and the
middle child, Jenny, grew up as English children. To them
Josephine Ahmansson was an unofficial "Aunty," as well as
the housekeeper who relieved Madame Lind-Goldschmidt
of all domestic details in running the household. Otto managed his wife's financial affairs, shielding her from worry
and annoyance, and they frequently gave concerts together.
She was intensely proud of his accomplishments as a musician. After taking up residence in London, he became Vice
Principal of the Royal Academy of Music, and he later
founded and directed the famous Bach Choir.

Their music drew the couple ever closer together, but
their marriage presented problems which less noted persons
could have avoided. Jenny resented it when her English
neighbors dubbed Otto "the Prince Consort of song."
There was a decided resemblance between him and Prince
Albert, the handsome consort of Queen Victoria; but Madame Lind-Goldschmidt wanted her husband placed first,
not second, in their home.

Much more serious was the envy which over the years
prompted a number of libelous statements in the press. The
Goldschmidts finally took legal action against the publish-
ers. Several English neighbors testified at the trial as to their
knowledge of the couple's happiness, and Jenny took the
witness box to deny that her husband had wasted her fortune. On the contrary, her financial position had improved
under his management. The outcome was to vindicate Otto,
but only after a long period of worry and strain.

Unlike an earlier suitor, Captain Harris, Otto approved
of his wife's gifts to worthy causes. It has been estimated

that she gave away half a million dollars during her lifetime. Her personal earnings from the American tour were set aside in "a private and special fund" for the benefit of the youth of Sweden. Paradoxically, the man who had made this fund possible was a business failure within five years after his star left America. When a bad investment swept away Mr. Barnums fortune, he went to London to promote some new enterprise.

Otto called on him there. Jenny was ready to offer him financial assistance, which Mr. Barnum gratefully but firmly declined. His friends need not have worried. In seven years he was richer than before. P. T. Barnum's last big speculation, his circus, "The Greatest Show on Earth," opened in 1871. Nothing ever dimmed his zest for life, and the numerous editions of his entertaining autobiography were widely read. The story is told that a woman came up to him one day at the circus to congratulate him on the book.

"Oh, Mr. Barnum," she gushed, "you have no idea how much I have enjoyed reading your life."

"Madame," he replied, "you have no idea how much I have enjoyed living it."

In this autobiography he told of meeting his old friends, Benedict and Belletti, in London. Both musicians were a continuing success. Belletti had gone from one triumph to another, in opera, in concerts, and in oratorios. The time was soon coming when Benedict was to be knighted in recognition of his services as composer and musician in his adopted country.

Jules, or Sir Jules as he later would be called, was godfather to the Goldschmidts' oldest child. Jenny also renewed her acquaintance with Giovanni Belletti, and they sang together during concert tours of the British Isles before he retired to his native Italy. There is no record that he ever married.

Several of Jenny's associates on the American tour won success on the other side of the Atlantic. Charles Seyton was a partner in a brokerage firm. Le Grand Smith became an impresario in his own right, but a promising career was cut short when the ship on which he was returning home from England went down at sea in 1856.

The violinist, Joseph Burke, who lived on into the twentieth century, was several times president of the New York Philharmonic Society. He and Jenny corresponded occasionally for the rest of her life. In one of the earlier letters, dated 1853, she mentioned that her former secretary, Max Hjortzberg, had returned to the States, hoping to advance his fortunes as an engineer.

My poor Max—she wrote—*I knew he would have dark days before him.*

Evidently the young man's hot temper was still getting him into trouble.

As for that other young man who, though he never saw America, was indirectly responsible for Jenny's tour, he has entered into a merciful oblivion. So far as is known, Jenny never heard of Captain Claudius Harris again. He is remembered only because he once went to sleep while a "nightingale" was singing.

During the Goldschmidts' years in England they lived in several different houses. Jenny's favorite and final home was "Wynd's Point," tucked away in a hollow of the Malvern Hills. She loved the many-gabled cottage with the odd Swedish porch, the little semicircular music room decorated in gold and gray, and the rustic arbor she had built as a surprise for her husband.

Always deeply religious, Jenny became more and more introspective as she grew older. One day a friend found her, during a visit to the beach, resting on the sands and gazing at the sunset. The Bible she had been reading lay open in her lap.

The friend's thoughts went back forty years.

"Oh, Madame Goldschmidt, how was it that you abandoned the stage at the height of your success?" she asked.

"When every day, it made me think less of *this?*" She glanced at her Bible, then at the sunset. "And nothing at all of *that?* What else could I do?"

Until the end of her life she was a person of many contradictions, and it was Otto who had to smooth over many an awkward situation. Unwanted visitors often found her an austere woman who resented intrusions on her privacy. On one occasion she came downstairs to find several strangers in her drawing room.

"What do you want?" she demanded.

"We just wanted to see you."

Jenny turned around. "Here is my back," she said. She wheeled and faced them. "Here is my front. Now you have seen me."

With that she turned and went upstairs, leaving her abashed callers to find their way out alone.

She was always uneasy lest she be stared at—wrote Mrs. Simpson, the daughter of Mr. Senior, Jenny's old friend and solicitor—*If any presumptuous one might peep in at the* [garden] *gate, she would instantly open a large red umbrella and shelter herself.*

On other occasions she could be quite gay. In an intimate group of friends she sometimes convulsed them as she mimicked some of the well-known actors of the day. She delighted in showing the many handsome gifts she had received. She would point to her mouth.

"And they all came out of here," she laughed.

Jenny Lind's daughter, Jenny, also had a promising voice, but was not interested in a career. She married Raymond Maude. By that time the other Goldschmidt children had also grown up and left home. Walter was in a London office. Ernest, later a lieutenant colonel in the British Army, who lived to fight in World War I, was studying in Germany.

After the younger Jenny's marriage, Madame Goldschmidt became the first professor of singing in the new Royal College of Music. Just as she had been a great singer, she was a great teacher. Only failing health forced her to give up the post, and she turned, as always, to her devoted husband.

My own dear love is my all—she wrote to a friend—
How dear he is to me, no one knows.

The great prima donna had found what she wanted most in life, but there must have been times when she missed her one-time glory. The knowledge that her powers were waning could not fail to sadden her, but there was a hint of the old magic to the end. The fact that her voice was not what it had once been did not seem to matter. Said one friend: *Jenny Lind still has her soul.*

Though Jenny lived to be sixty-seven, in the words of Sir Jules Benedict: *She is remembered as ever young.* In the wake of the sorrow that followed the news of her death in November, 1887, precious memories were revived. This was true of kings and statesmen and sophisticated music lovers. It was also true of many humble folk who may never have attended but one concert in their lives, a concert by Jenny Lind. Hearing her sing had been an unforgettable experience for all kinds of people on both sides of the Atlantic.

During her last days, her thoughts were often on America. One of her final requests was that a patchwork quilt presented to her years earlier by some children in the United States be buried with her, and her husband saw that it was done.

Otto Goldschmidt never remarried. As devoted to Jenny's memory as he had been devoted to her in life, he gave much time and thought to assembling his late wife's papers and supervising the preparation of the large, two-volume, definitive biography by two friends, H.S. Holland and W.S. Rockstro.

In a shorter, more personal book, written by the daughter, Jenny Goldschmidt Maude, Mrs. Maude recalled that on several occasions her mother had been urged to revisit the United States. One letter received during the American Civil War came from the Ladies Committee of the United States Sanitary Commission, an organization similar to the later Red Cross. The president of the committee suggested that Madame Lind-Goldschmidt give a series of benefit concerts for the relief of wounded soldiers and their dependent families. Though the invitation could not be accepted for reasons of health, it was a letter to be treasured. In a single paragraph it explained the continuing appeal of Jenny Lind for Jenny Lind's America:

The memories of your voice are still fresh in the hearts of Americans. Still more precious to them is the recollection that that voice was always exerted for benevolent and humane objects. The welcome that would await you is such as could only be given to Jenny Lind whose harmonious notes have lingered in our ears, not only because they were delicious, but because they were the outpouring of a pure and gentle heart.

The Jenny Lind Calendar

Before she came to America

1820	Jenny Lind, daughter of Anne-Marie and Niklas Lind, was born (Oct. 6) at Stockholm, Sweden.
1821–29	Her parents were poor, and part of her childhood was spent in two foster homes. At the age of nine, it was discovered that she had a remarkable voice, and the directors of the Royal Opera in Stockholm arranged to have her educated at the expense of the Swedish government.
1830–37	Jenny Lind studied at the school connected with the Royal Opera and also took children's parts in plays.
1838	Five months after her seventeenth birthday, she made her debut (March 7) in the part of Agatha in *Der Freischütz* ("The Freeshooter") by Carl Maria von Weber. An overnight success, she soon became known as the "Swedish Nightingale." During the next two and a half years she sang in various operatic roles and made concert tours in Sweden. Though a coloratura soprano, her voice had a remarkable range and was also effective in dramatic and lyric soprano roles.
1841–42	She studied for ten months in Paris under the famous Spanish singing master, Manuel Garcia.

1843   She toured Finland and visited Copenhagen where she met Hans Christian Andersen for the first time.

1844–47   She appeared in a number of operatic roles in cities of Germany and Austria.

1848–49   Her earlier successes were repeated in England, but in 1849 she announced that she would retire from the stage. Already well known for her charities, she planned to give a series of concerts to raise money to establish music scholarships for young people in her native land.

1850   In January, while resting in Germany, Jenny Lind signed an agreement to sing in concerts in the United States under the auspices of P. T. Barnum, the American showman. She sailed (Aug. 19) from Liverpool, England, on the steamer *Atlantic*.

Her twenty-one months in America

September With the assistance of two European artists, Jules
1850   Benedict, pianist and orchestra conductor, and Giovanni Belletti, baritone, Jenny Lind gave her first American concert (Sept. 11) in New York City. It took place in Castle Garden, a huge auditorium, formerly a fort, at the southern end of Manhattan, at the point known as Battery Park today. After five more concerts she moved on (Sept. 26) to Boston.

October   Eight concerts were given in Boston, with a side
1850   trip to sing in Providence, Rhode Island. En route to Philadelphia, to fulfill an engagement there, Jenny Lind and several other members of the company visited Iranistan, the palatial home of P. T. Barnum, their manager, in Bridgeport, Connecticut.

November 1850	After fourteen more concerts in New York City, the troupe left (Nov. 25) to go on tour, beginning with a second appearance in Philadelphia. On this tour seventeen cities and towns would be visited and more than four thousand miles traveled.
December 1850	Concerts were given in Baltimore, Washington, D. C., Richmond, Virginia, and Charleston, South Carolina.
January 1851	The troupe arrived (Jan. 5) in Havana, Cuba, where four concerts preceded a much-needed rest.
February 1851	Jenny Lind and party left Havana (Feb. 3) for New Orleans, where twelve concerts were given.
March 1851	The party left New Orleans (Mar. 10) on the steamboat *Magnolia*. On the voyage up the Mississippi River, brief stops were made to give concerts in Natchez, Mississippi, and Memphis, Tennessee. After five concerts in St. Louis, Missouri, the company arrived in Nashville, Tennessee (Mar. 30).
April 1851	Following two Nashville concerts, Jenny Lind with several friends took a stagecoach for Louisville, Kentucky, stopping en route to visit Mammoth Cave. While in Louisville, Señor Salvi, Spanish tenor, arrived to join the company. After a third concert there (Apr. 9) they boarded another steamboat, stopping en route to sing in the village of Madison, Indiana. Four concerts in Cincinnatti were followed by one in Wheeling, West Virginia, and one in Pittsburgh, Pennsylvania (Apr. 25).
May 1851	After an absence of more than five months, Jenny Lind and her troupe returned to New York, where fourteen concerts were given. Otto Goldschmidt, a young German pianist of Jewish heritage, arrived to be her accompanist.

June 1851	Jenny Lind was singing in Philadelphia when, at the end of her ninety-third concert, she and P. T. Barnum terminated their agreement by mutual consent (June 9).
July 1851	Jenny Lind, with a company much reduced in size, proceeded to give concerts under her own management. Her business assistants booked concerts for her in Springfield, Massachusetts; the nearby village of Northampton; Hartford, Connecticut; and several cities in New York state: Utica, Auburn, Rochester, Syracuse, Albany and Buffalo.
August- September 1851	Jenny Lind interrupted a vacation on the Canadian side of Niagara Falls to travel to New York City (Aug. 3), where she saw Jules Benedict and Giovanni Belletti off for Europe. She then returned to Niagara Falls to spend several more weeks.
October- November 1851	Jenny Lind resumed her tour with a benefit concert in Buffalo (Oct. 16). After singing in Toronto, Canada; Cleveland and Cincinnati, Ohio; and Pittsburgh and Harrisburg, Pennsylvania, she returned to Boston (Nov. 21).
December 1851	After a fourth concert in Boston (Dec. 5), she sang in Worcester, Massachusetts; New Haven, Connecticut; and Philadelphia. Back in New York in time for Christmas, the newspapers were informed that she would give a farewell concert (Dec. 31) and sail for Europe in January. The farewell concert was canceled when she received word of her mother's death.
January 1852	Instead of sailing for Liverpool as planned, Jenny Lind returned to Boston with her accompanist, Otto Goldschmidt, to whom she had become engaged.
February 1852	Jenny Lind was married (Feb. 5) to Otto Goldschmidt at the home of Mr. Samuel Ward in

Louisburg Square on Beacon Hill in Boston. After the ceremony the couple left to spend their honeymoon in nearby Northampton.

March-
May
1852

While still on her honeymoon, Jenny made her first public appearance as Madame Goldschmidt in a benefit recital (May 6) at the Town Hall in Northampton. Three farewell concerts were given later that month in New York City, the final (May 24) in Castle Garden. A few days later she and her husband sailed for Europe.

After she left America

1852–57

Jenny Lind and her husband Otto Goldschmidt made their home in Germany where their son Walter and daughter Jenny were born. The couple frequently appeared in concerts together both on the continent and in Great Britain.

1858

The couple decided to make their permanent home in England.

1861–82

After the birth of a third child, Ernst (1861), Jenny Lind with her husband embarked on another concert tour. For a number of years, on special occasions, she continued to sing in concerts and oratorios, donating the money earned to worthy causes. After moving to England, and living in several different houses, the Goldschmidts purchased "Wynd's Point" (1878) in the Malvern Mills.

1883–86

It was at Malvern Hills that Jenny gave her final concert (1883) for the benefit of the Railway Servants' Benevolent Fund. She taught singing at the Royal College of Music.

1887

Jenny Lind, aged sixty-seven, died at Wynd's Point November 2.

1894

In April a medallion in memory of the Swedish Nightingale was unveiled in Westminster Abbey.

1920   The Centennial of her birth was observed in several countries. In New York City, on her 100th birthday (Oct. 6), a memorial concert was given in Carnegie Hall, with Frieda Hempel, another coloratura soprano, singing the same songs Jenny Lind had sung at her first American concert in Castle Garden.

1970   Jenny Lind's Sesquicentennial finds her still remembered and loved. Events during the year include a memorial concert in her native Stockholm and a revival in New York's Metropolitan Opera House of *Der Freischutz*, the opera in which Jenny Lind had scored her first great triumph.

Jenny Lind Memorabilia

Letters to and by Jenny Lind; souvenir programs portraits and sculptured busts, contemporary newspaper clippings, medals struck in her honor, personal belongings and other Lind memorabilia may be found in a number of museums. These include the Museum of the City of New York; New York Historical Society; Barnum Museum of Tufts University; Barnum Museum of Bridgeport, Conn.; Maryland Historical Society (Baltimore); Missouri Historical Society (St. Louis); Rochester (N.Y.) Historical Society; Buffalo (N.Y.) and Erie County Historical Society; Connecticut Valley Historical Museum and Library (Springfield, Mass.); Stephen Foster Memorial Commission (White Springs, Fla.); American Swedish Historical Foundation (Philadelphia).

About the Author

Frances Cavanah grew up in Indiana, graduated from DePauw University, and then joined the staff of *Child Life* magazine. After fifteen years with that magazine, she was biography editor of an encyclopedia and then director of biographies for a textbook publisher. During this time she also edited several anthologies and wrote books and stories of her own.

She early decided that there could be no greater satisfaction than writing for young people. When she combined this with her love of history, she produced a number of books that have earned her acclaim and brought her a wide following.

Her enthusiasm for Jenny Lind resulted in two previous books about the Swedish Nightingale, *Two Loves for Jenny Lind* and *Jenny Lind and Her Listening Cat.* Her absorbing interest in American history produced *Our Country's Story, Meet the Presidents, Abe Lincoln Gets His Chance, Adventure in Courage, the Story of Theodore Roosevelt; Triumphant Adventure, the Story of Franklin Delano Roosevelt;* and *We Came to America,* which showed how this country appeared to the succession of immigrants who arrived on our shores. One of her most recent books is *Freedom Encyclopedia: American Liberties in the Making.*

Miss Cavanah lives in Washington, D.C., not too far from the Library of Congress where she spends hours in fascinating research.